Designer Series Introduction

Distinctive Home Designs - Home Plans Designer Series is a collection of best-selling home plans from some of the nation's leading designers and architects. Only quality plans with sound design, functional layout, energy efficiency and affordability have been selected.

This plan book covers a wide range of architectural styles in a popular range of sizes. A broad assortment is presented to match a wide variety of lifestyles and budgets. Each design page features floor plans, a front view of the house, and a list of special features. All floor plans show room dimensions, exterior dimensions and the interior square footage of the home.

Technical Specifications - At the time the construction drawings were prepared, every effort was made to ensure that these plans and specifications meet nationally recognized building codes (BOCA, Southern Building Code Congress and others). Because national building codes change or vary from area to area some drawing modifications and/or the assistance of a professional designer or architect may be necessary to comply with your local codes or to accommodate specific building site conditions. We advise you to consult with your local building official for information regarding codes governing your area.

Detailed Material Lists - An accurate material list showing the quantity, dimensions, and description of the major building materials necessary to construct your new home can save you a considerable amount of time and money. Please check Home Plan Index on page 318-319 for availability.

Blueprint Ordering - Fast and Easy - Your ordering is made simple by following the instructions on page 320. See page 319 for more information on what type of blueprint packages are available and how many plan sets to order.

Your Home, Your Way - The blueprints you receive are a master plan for building your new home. They start you on your way to what may well be the most rewarding experience of your life.

Contents

Cover home is plan #X26-GH-34901 is featured on page 186. Photo courtesy of Garlinghouse.

Home Plans Designer Series is published by Home Design Alternatives, Inc. (HDA, Inc.) 4390 Green Ash Drive, St. Louis, MO 63045. All rights reserved. Reproduction in whole or in part without written permission of the publisher is prohibited. Printed in U.S.A © 2003.

Photos Courtesy of Top to bottom: plan #X26-0417 - HDA, Inc., plan #X26-DB2461 - Design Basics, Inc., plan #X26-NDG-142 - Nelson Design Group, plan #X26-GH-34901 - Garlinghouse, plan #X26-0711 - HDA, Inc., plan #X26-MG-96151 - Mike Garrell, plan #X26-0159 - HDA, Inc.

Current Printing 5 4 3 2

Plan #X26-DB2461

Plan #X26-NDG-142

Plan #X26-GH-34901

Plan #X26-0711

Plan #X26-MG-96151

Plan #X26-0159

QUICK AND EASY CUSTOMIZING
MAKE CHANGES TO YOUR HOME PLAN IN 4 STEPS

HERE'S AN **AFFORDABLE** AND **EFFICIENT** WAY TO MAKE CHANGES TO YOUR PLAN.

1 **Select the house plan that most closely meets your needs.** Purchase of a reproducible master is necessary in order to make changes to a plan.

2 **Call 1-800-373-2646 to place your order.** Tell the sales representative you're interested in customizing a plan. A $50 refundable consultation fee will be charged. You will then be instructed to complete a customization checklist indicating all the changes you wish to make to your plan. You may attach sketches if necessary. If you proceed with the custom changes the $50 will be credited to the total amount charged.

3 **FAX the completed customization checklist to our design consultant** at 1-866-477-5173 or e-mail **custom@drummonddesigns.com.** Within *24-48 business hours you will be provided with a written cost estimate to modify your plan. Our design consultant will contact you by phone if you wish to discuss any of your changes in greater detail.

4 **Once you approve the estimate,** a 75% retainer fee is collected and customization work gets underway. Preliminary drawings can usually be completed within *5-10 business days. Following approval of the preliminary drawings your design changes are completed within *5-10 business days. Your remaining 25% balance due is collected prior to shipment of your completed drawings. You will be shipped five sets of revised blueprints or a reproducible master, plus a customized materials list if required.

*Terms are subject to change without notice.

BEFORE
Plan 2829

Customized Version of Plan 2829

AFTER

Sample Modification Pricing Guide

The average prices specified below are provided as examples only. They refer to the most commonly requested changes, and are subject to change without notice. Prices for changes will vary or differ, from the prices below, depending on the number of modifications requested, the plan size, style, quality of original plan, format provided to us (originally drawn by hand or computer), and method of design used by the original designer. To obtain a detailed cost estimate or to get more information, please contact us.

Sample Modification Pricing Guide	*Average Cost
Adding or removing living space	Quote required
Adding or removing a garage	Starting at $400
Garage: Front entry to side load or vice versa	Starting at $300
Adding a screened porch	Starting at $280
Adding a bonus room in the attic	Starting at $450
Changing full basement to crawl space or vice versa	Starting at $220
Changing full basement to slab or vice versa	Starting at $260
Changing exterior building material	Starting at $200
Changing roof lines	Starting at $360
Adjusting ceiling height	Starting at $280
Adding, moving or removing an exterior opening	$65 per opening
Adding or removing a fireplace	Starting at $90
Modifying a non-bearing wall or room	$65 per room
Changing exterior walls from 2"x4" to 2"x6"	Starting at $200
Redesigning a bathroom or a kitchen	Starting at $120
Reverse plan right reading	Quote required
Adapting plans for local building code requirements	Quote required
Engineering and Architectural stamping and services	Quote required
Adjust plan for handicapped accessibility	Quote required
Interactive Illustrations (choices of exterior materials)	Quote required
Metric conversion of home plan	Starting at $400

*Prices and Terms are subject to change without notice.

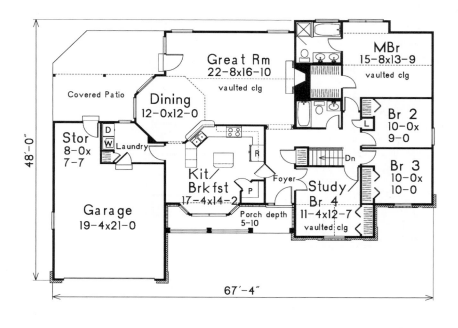

Classic Exterior Employs Innovative Planning

Special features

- 1,791 total square feet of living area

- Vaulted great room and octagon-shaped dining area enjoy views of covered patio

- Kitchen features a pass-through to dining area, center island, large walk-in pantry and breakfast room with large bay window

- Master bedroom is vaulted with sitting area

- 4 bedrooms, 2 baths, 2-car garage with storage

- Basement foundation, drawings also include crawl space and slab foundations

Ranch Offers
Country Elegance

Special features

- 1,787 total square feet of living area
- Large great room with fireplace and vaulted ceiling features three large skylights and windows galore
- Cooking is sure to be a pleasure in this L-shaped well-appointed kitchen which includes bayed breakfast area with access to rear deck
- Every bedroom offers a spacious walk-in closet with a convenient laundry room just steps away
- 415 square feet of optional living area on the lower level
- 3 bedrooms, 2 baths, 2-car rear entry garage
- Walk-out basement foundation

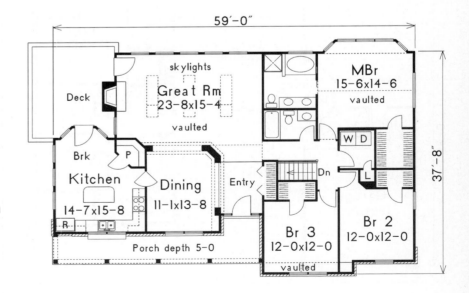

Atrium's Dramatic Ambiance, Compliments Of Windows

Special features

- 1,721 total square feet of living area
- Roof dormers add great curb appeal
- Vaulted dining and great rooms immersed in light from atrium window wall
- Breakfast room opens onto covered porch
- Functionally designed kitchen
- 3 bedrooms, 2 baths, 3-car garage
- Walk-out basement foundation, drawings also include crawl space and slab foundations

Rear View

Classic Ranch Has Grand Appeal With Expansive Porch

Special features

- 1,400 total square feet of living area
- Master bedroom is secluded for privacy
- Large utility room with additional cabinet space
- Covered porch provides an outdoor seating area
- Roof dormers add great curb appeal
- Vaulted ceilings in living room and master bedroom
- Oversized two-car garage with storage
- 3 bedrooms, 2 baths, 2-car garage
- Basement foundation, drawings also include crawl space foundation

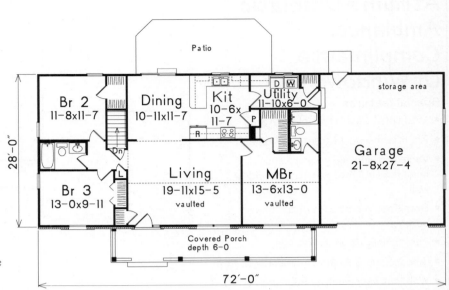

Picture Perfect For A Country Setting

Special features

- 2,967 total square feet of living area

- An exterior with charm graced with country porch and multiple arched projected box windows

- Dining area is oversized and adjoins a fully equipped kitchen with walk-in pantry

- Two bay windows light up the enormous informal living area to the rear

- 4 bedrooms, 3 1/2 baths, 3-car side entry garage

- Basement foundation

- 1,450 square feet on the first floor and 1,517 square feet on the second floor

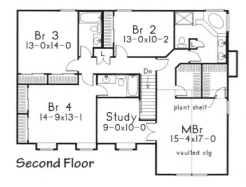

Second Floor

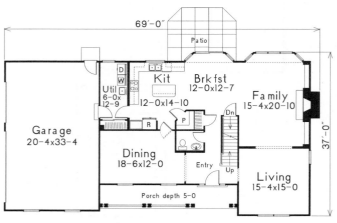

First Floor

Rear View

First Floor

55'-8"

Atrium below

Dn

Dining Area

Kit
10-2x
11-9

Garage
22-0x11-9

Great Rm
18-0x21-8
vaulted

Laundry

D W

Cover porch depth 6-0

46'-0"

Br 2
11-4x12-6

MBr
12-8x15-0

Optional Lower Level

Up

Patio

Family Rm
25-0x21-4

Unexcavated

Unfinished Basement

Tranquility Of An Atrium Cottage

Special features

- 1,384 total square feet of living area
- Wrap-around country porch for peaceful evenings
- Vaulted great room enjoys a large bay window, stone fireplace, pass-through kitchen and awesome rear views through atrium window wall
- Master bedroom features double entry doors, walk-in closet and a fabulous bath
- Atrium open to 611 square feet of optional living area below
- 2 bedrooms, 2 baths, 1-car side entry garage
- Walk-out basement foundation

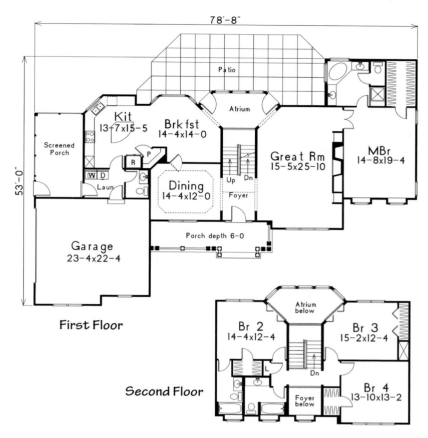

78'-8"

Patio

Kit
13-7x15-5

Brk fst
14-4x14-0

Atrium

Screened
Porch

53'-0"

W | D

R

P

Laun

Dining
14-4x12-0

Up | Dn

Foyer

Great Rm
15-5x25-10

MBr
14-8x19-4

Garage
23-4x22-4

Porch depth 6-0

First Floor

Atrium
below

Br 2
14-4x12-4

Br 3
15-2x12-4

L

Dn

Foyer
below

Br 4
13-10x13-2

Second Floor

Two-Story Atrium For Great Views

Special features

- 2,900 total square feet of living area
- Elegant entry foyer leads to balcony overlook of vaulted two-story atrium
- Spacious kitchen features an island breakfast bar, walk-in pantry, bayed breakfast room and adjoining screened porch
- Two large second floor bedrooms and stair balconies overlook a sun drenched two-story vaulted atrium
- 4 bedrooms, 3 1/2 baths, 2-car side entry garage
- Basement foundation
- 1,835 square feet on the first floor and 1,065 square feet on the second floor

Rambling Country Bungalow

Special features

- 1,475 total square feet of living area
- Family room features a high ceiling and prominent corner fireplace
- Kitchen with island counter and garden window makes a convenient connection between the family and dining rooms
- Hallway leads to three bedrooms all with large walk-in closets
- Covered breezeway joins main house and garage
- Full-width covered porch entry lends a country touch
- 3 bedrooms, 2 baths, 2-car side entry garage
- Slab foundation, drawings also include crawl space foundation

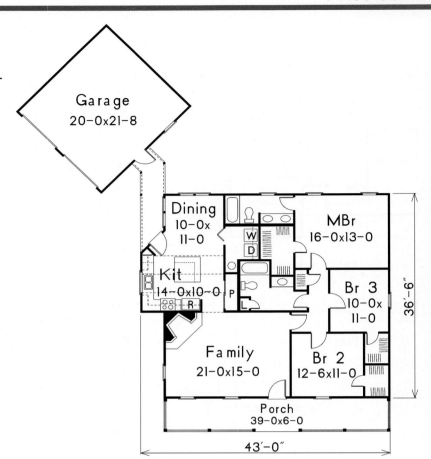

Plan #X26-0449

Price Code D

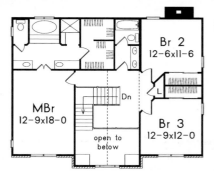

Second Floor

Br 2
12-6x11-6

MBr
12-9x18-0

Dn

open to
below

Br 3
12-9x12-0

Charming House, Spacious And Functional

Special features

- 2,505 total square feet of living area

- The garage features extra storage area and ample work space

- Laundry room accessible from the garage and the outdoors

- Deluxe raised tub and immense walk-in closet grace master bath

- 3 bedrooms, 2 1/2 baths, 2-car side entry garage

- Basement foundation, drawings also include crawl space foundation

- 1,436 square feet on the first floor and 1,069 square feet on the second floor

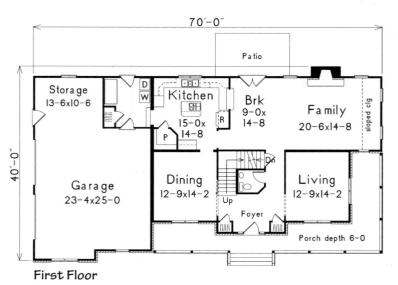

70'-0"

Patio

40'-0"

Storage
13-6x10-6

Kitchen
15-0x
14-8

Brk
9-0x
14-8

Family
20-6x14-8

sloped clg

Garage
23-4x25-0

Dining
12-9x14-2

Living
12-9x14-2

Up

Foyer

Porch depth 6-0

First Floor

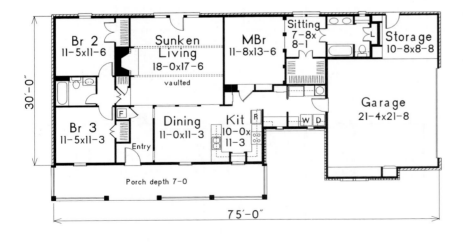

Charming Country Styling In This Ranch

Special features

- 1,600 total square feet of living area
- Impressive sunken living room has massive stone fireplace and 16' vaulted ceilings
- Dining room conveniently located next to kitchen and divided for privacy
- Energy efficient home with 2" x 6" exterior walls
- Special amenities include sewing room, glass shelves in kitchen and master bath and a large utility area
- Sunken master bedroom features a distinctive sitting room
- 3 bedrooms, 2 baths, 2-car side entry garage
- Slab foundation, drawings also include crawl space and basement foundations

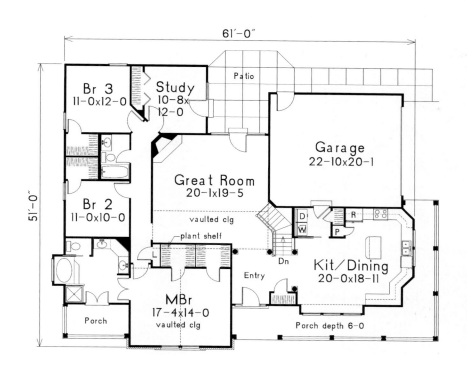

Country Home With Front Orientation

Special features

- 2,029 total square feet of living area

- Stonework, gables, roof dormer and double porches create a country flavor

- Kitchen enjoys extravagant cabinetry and counterspace in a bay, island snack bar, built-in pantry and cheery dining area with multiple tall windows

- Angled stair descends from entry with wood columns and is open to vaulted great room with corner fireplace

- Master bedroom boasts two walk-in closets, double-doors leading to an opulent master bath and private porch

- 4 bedrooms, 2 baths, 2-car side entry garage

- Basement foundation, drawings also include crawl space and slab foundations

Duo Atrium For Fantastic Views

Special features

- 2,125 total square feet of living area

- A cozy porch leads to the vaulted great room with fireplace through the entry which has a walk-in closet and bath

- Large and well-arranged kitchen offers spectacular views from its cantilevered sink cabinetry through a two-story atrium window wall

- Master bedroom boasts a sitting room, large walk-in closet and bath with garden tub overhanging a brightly lit atrium

- The lower level features an optional study and family room with walk-in bar and full bath below the kitchen consisting of 1,047 additional square feet

- 3 bedrooms, 2 1/2 baths, 2-car side entry garage

- Walk-out basement foundation

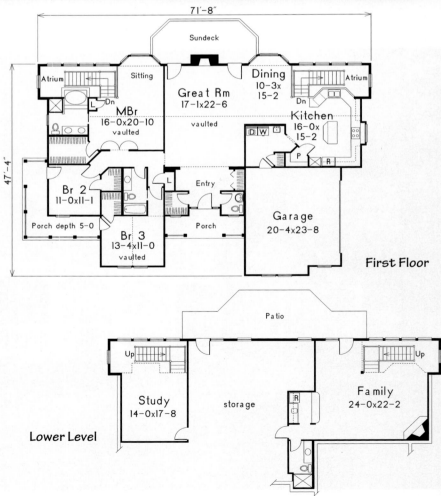

First Floor

Lower Level

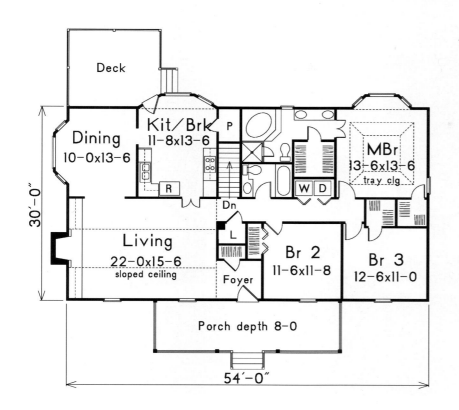

Deck

Dining
10-0x13-6

Kit/Brk
11-8x13-6

P

MBr
13-6x13-6
tray clg

30'-0"

Living
22-0x15-6
sloped ceiling

L

Dn

W D

Br 2
11-6x11-8

Br 3
12-6x11-0

Foyer

Porch depth 8-0

54'-0"

Bay Window Graces Luxury Master Bedroom

Special features

- 1,668 total square feet of living area
- Large bay windows in breakfast area, master bedroom and dining room
- Extensive walk-in closets and storage spaces throughout the home
- Handy entry covered porch
- Large living room has fireplace, built-in bookshelves and sloped ceiling
- 3 bedrooms, 2 baths, 2-car drive under garage
- Basement foundation

Atrium Ranch With True Pizzazz

Special features

- 2,397 total square feet of living area
- A grand entry porch leads to a dramatic vaulted foyer with plant shelf open to great room
- The great room enjoys a 12' vaulted ceiling, atrium featuring 2 1/2 story windows and fireplace with flanking bookshelves
- A conveniently located sun-room and side porch adjoin the breakfast room and garage
- 898 square feet of optional lower living area on the lower level with family room, bedroom #4 and bath
- 3 bedrooms, 2 baths, 3-car side entry garage
- Walk-out basement foundation

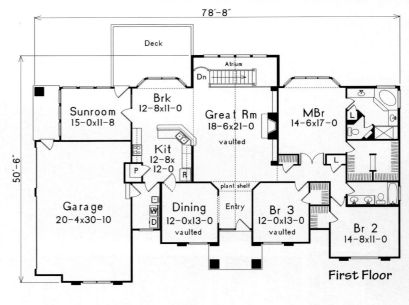

First Floor

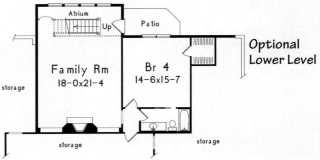

Optional Lower Level

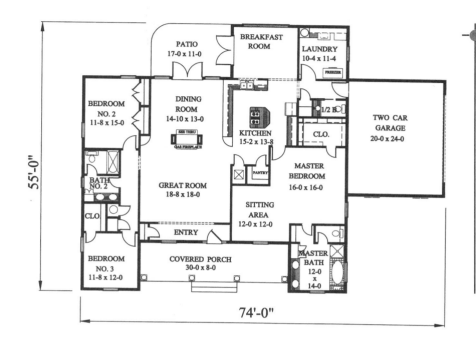

BEDROOM
NO. 2
11-8 x 15-0

PATIO
17-0 x 11-0

BREAKFAST
ROOM

LAUNDRY
10-4 x 11-4

FREEZER

DINING
ROOM
14-10 x 13-0

SEE THRU
GAS FIREPLACE

KITCHEN
15-2 x 13-8

1/2 B

CLO.

TWO CAR
GARAGE
20-0 x 24-0

BATH
NO. 2

CLO.

GREAT ROOM
18-8 x 18-0

PANTRY

MASTER
BEDROOM
16-0 x 16-0

SITTING
AREA
12-0 x 12-0

ENTRY

BEDROOM
NO. 3
11-8 x 12-0

COVERED PORCH
30-0 x 8-0

MASTER
BATH
12-0
x
14-0

55'-0"

74'-0"

Unique Master Suite

Special features

- 2,340 total square feet of living area
- Great room shares a see-through fireplace with the dining room
- Bedrooms #2 and #3 share a split bath
- Enormous sitting area in master bedroom could easily be converted to a study or even a nursery
- 3 bedrooms, 2 1/2 baths, 2-car side entry garage
- Crawl space or slab foundation, please specify when ordering

Quaint Box
Window Seat

Special features

- 1,665 total square feet of living area
- Oversized family room has corner fireplace and double-doors leading to patio
- Bedroom locations give privacy from gathering areas
- 3 bedrooms, 2 baths, 2-car garage
- Slab foundation

Width: 50'-0"
Depth: 55'-0"

Lovely Ranch Home

Special features

- 1,123 total square feet of living area
- Eating bar in kitchen extends dining area
- Dining area and great room flow together creating a sense of spaciousness
- Master suite has privacy from other bedrooms as well as a private bath
- Utility room is conveniently located near kitchen
- 3 bedrooms, 2 baths
- Crawl space or slab foundation, please specify when ordering

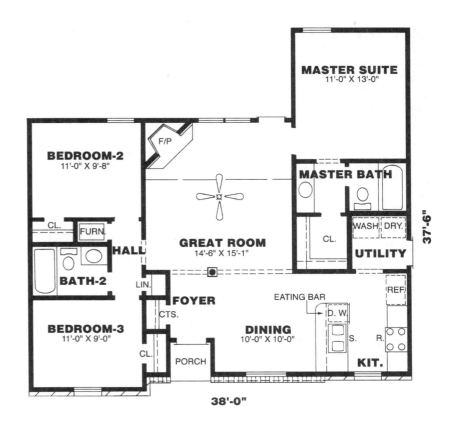

Cozy Country Farmhouse

Special features

- 920 total square feet of living area

- Bath has extra space for washer and dryer

- Plenty of seating for dining at kitchen counter

- Energy efficient 2" x 6" exterior walls

- 2 bedrooms, 1 bath

- Basement foundation

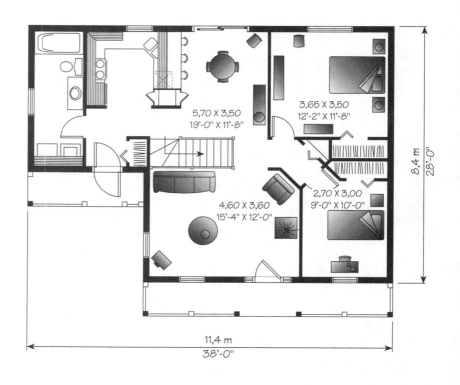

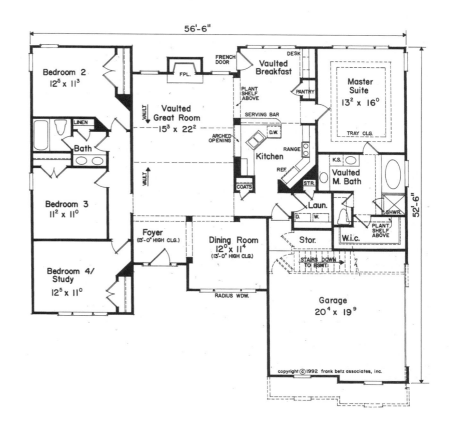

Plenty Of Detail

Special features

- 1,945 total square feet of living area
- Master suite separated from other bedrooms for privacy
- Vaulted breakfast room is directly off great room
- Kitchen includes a built-in desk area
- Elegant dining room has an arched window
- 4 bedrooms, 2 baths, 2-car side entry garage
- Walk-out basement, crawl space or slab foundation, please specify when ordering

Uncommon Style With This Ranch

Special features

- 1,787 total square feet of living area,

- Skylights brighten screened porch which connects to family room and deck outdoors

- Master bedroom features a comfortable sitting area, large private bath and direct access to screened porch

- Kitchen has serving bar which extends dining into family room

- 3 bedrooms, 2 baths, 2-car side entry garage

- Basement, crawl space or slab foundation, please specify when ordering

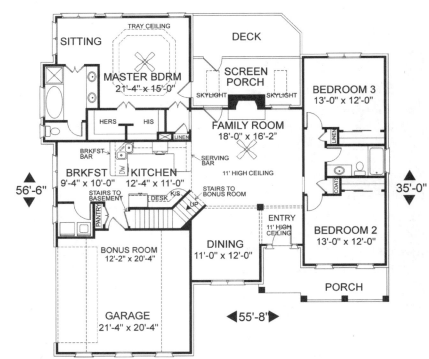

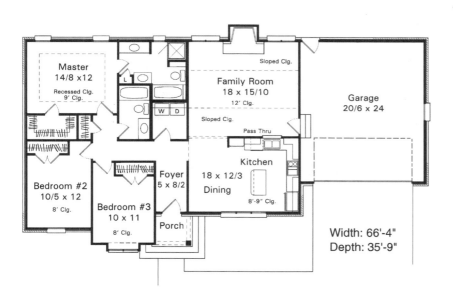

Master
14/8 x12
Recessed Clg.
9' Clg.

Family Room
18 x 15/10
12' Clg.

Sloped Clg.

Sloped Clg.

Garage
20/6 x 24

Bedroom #2
10/5 x 12
8' Clg.

Bedroom #3
10 x 11
8' Clg.

Foyer
5 x 8/2

Porch

W   D

Pass Thru

Kitchen
18 x 12/3
Dining
8'-9" Clg.

Width: 66'-4"
Depth: 35'-9"

Handy Kitchen Pass-Through

Special features

- 1,388 total square feet of living area
- Family room includes enormous fireplace centered between two sets of windows
- Kitchen has center island for eat-in dining and combines with dining area for openness
- 3 bedrooms, 2 baths, 2-car garage
- Crawl space or slab foundation, please specify when ordering

Prestige Abounds In A Classic Ranch

Special features

- 2,723 total square feet of living area
- Large porch invites you into an elegant foyer which accesses a vaulted study with private hall and coat closet
- Great room is second to none, comprised of fireplace, built-in shelves, vaulted ceiling and a 1 1/2 story window wall
- A spectacular hearth room with vaulted ceiling and masonry fireplace opens to an elaborate kitchen featuring two snack bars, cooking island and walk-in pantry
- 3 bedrooms, 2 1/2 baths, 3-car side entry garage
- Basement foundation

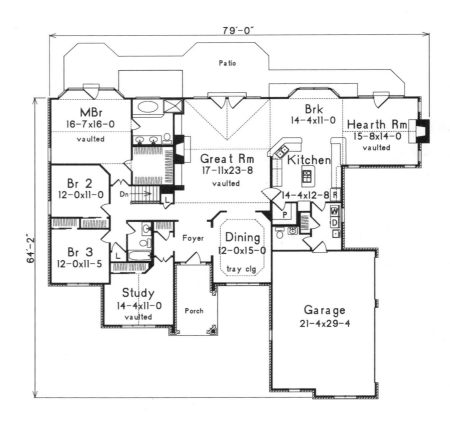

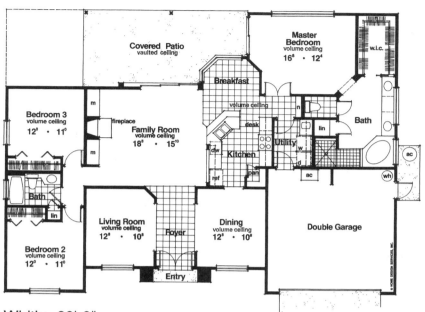

Width: 60'-0"
Depth: 45'-0"

Private Master Suite

Special features

- 1,783 total square feet of living area
- Grand foyer leading to family room
- Walk-in pantry in kitchen
- Master bath with step down "doorless" shower, huge vanity and large walk-in closet
- 3 bedrooms, 2 baths, 2-car garage
- Slab foundation

Inviting
Covered Verandas

Special features

- 1,830 total square feet of living area
- Inviting covered verandas in the front and rear of the home
- Great room has fireplace and cathedral ceiling
- Handy service porch allows easy access
- Master suite has vaulted ceiling and private bath
- 3 bedrooms, 2 baths, 3-car side entry garage
- Basement, crawl space or slab foundation, please specify when ordering

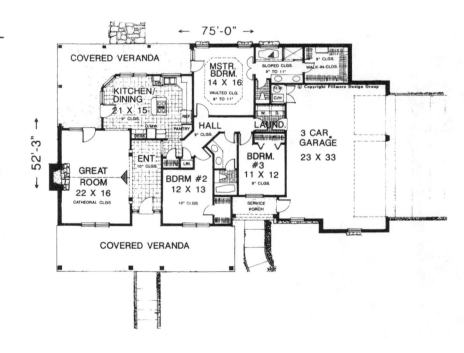

Split Bedroom, Drive Under Garage Design

Special features

- 1,268 total square feet of living area
- Raised gable porch is focal point creating dramatic look
- 10' ceilings throughout living and dining areas
- Open kitchen is well-designed
- Master suite offers tray ceiling and private bath with both a garden tub and a 4' shower
- 3 bedrooms, 2 baths, 2-car drive under garage
- Basement foundation

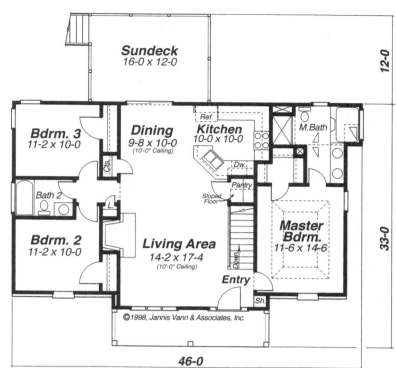

Second Floor

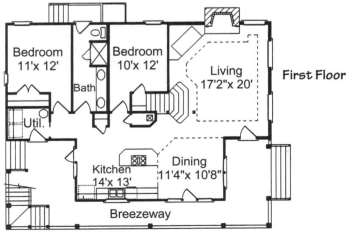

First Floor

Width: 46'-0"
Depth: 40'-6"

Southern Beachfront Styling

Special features

- 2,172 total square feet of living area
- 10' ceilings throughout the first floor
- 9' ceilings throughout the second floor
- Unique second floor loft makes great space for office or quiet space
- Unbelievable two floor breezeway surrounds home so every angle has access to a nice view
- 3 bedrooms, 2 baths, 2-car garage
- Slab, pier or crawl space foundation, please specify when ordering
- 1,252 square feet on the first floor and 920 square feet on the second floor

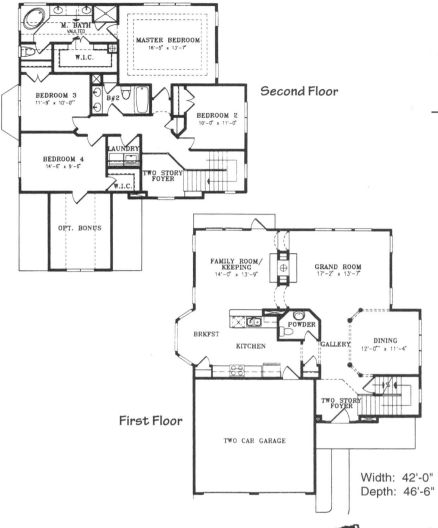

Second Floor

M. BATH
VAULTED

MASTER BEDROOM
16'-5" x 13'-7"

W.I.C.

BEDROOM 3
11'-9" x 10'-0"

B#2

BEDROOM 2
10'-0" x 11'-0"

LAUNDRY

BEDROOM 4
14'-6" x 9'-6"

TWO STORY
FOYER

W.I.C.

OPT. BONUS

FAMILY ROOM/
KEEPING
14'-0" x 13'-9"

GRAND ROOM
17'-2" x 13'-7"

BRKFST

POWDER

KITCHEN

GALLERY

DINING
12'-0" x 11'-4"

First Floor

TWO STORY
FOYER

TWO CAR GARAGE

Width: 42'-0"
Depth: 46'-6"

First Floor Creates Open Living

Special features

- 2,379 total square feet of living area
- Second floor laundry room is convenient to all bedrooms
- See-through fireplace enhances the family room and grand room
- Dining room accented with columns is open to grand room
- 4 bedrooms, 2 1/2 baths, 2-car garage
- Basement foundation
- 1,113 square feet on the first floor and 1,266 square feet on the second floor

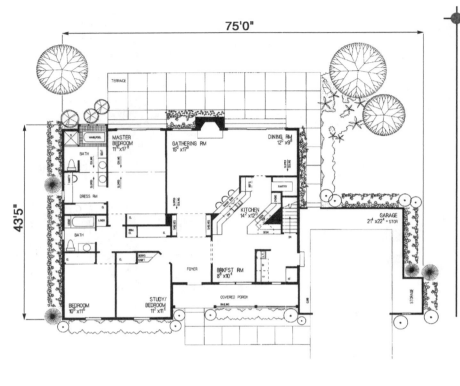

Charming One-Story Traditional

Special features

- 1,830 total square feet of living area
- A uniquely shaped galley-style kitchen shares a snack bar with the spacious gathering room with fireplace
- Dining room has sliding glass doors to the rear terrace as well as the master bedroom
- Master suite includes a luxury bath with a whirlpool tub and separate dressing room
- 3 bedrooms, 2 baths, 2-car garage
- Basement foundation

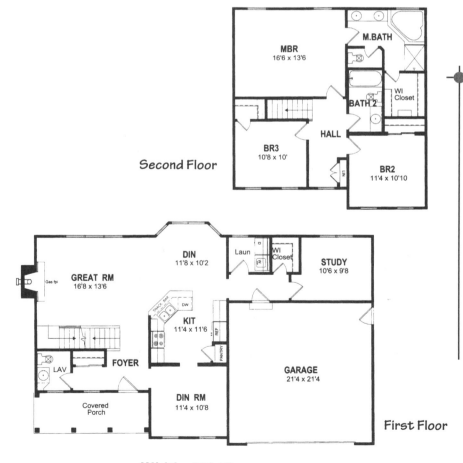

Second Floor

MBR
16'6 x 13'6

M.BATH

BATH 2

WI Closet

HALL

BR3
10'8 x 10'

BR2
11'4 x 10'10

GREAT RM
16'8 x 13'6

Gas fpl

DIN
11'8 x 10'2

Laun

WI Closet

STUDY
10'6 x 9'8

KIT
11'4 x 11'6

REF

PANTRY

DW

SNACK BAR

FOYER

LAV

GARAGE
21'4 x 21'4

Covered Porch

DIN RM
11'4 x 10'8

First Floor

Width: 52'-8"
Depth: 34'-0"

Plenty Of Closet Space

Special features

- 1,868 total square feet of living area
- Open floor plan creates an airy feeling
- Secluded study makes an ideal home office
- Large master bedroom has luxurious private bath with a walk-in closet
- Formal dining room has convenient access to kitchen
- 3 bedrooms, 2 1/2 baths, 2-car garage
- Basement foundation
- 1,020 square feet on the first floor and 848 square feet on the second floor

Cozy Traditional

Special features

- 1,310 total square feet of living area
- Family room features corner fireplace adding warmth
- Efficiently designed kitchen has a corner sink with windows
- Master bedroom includes large walk-in closet and private bath
- 3 bedrooms, 2 baths, 2-car garage
- Crawl space or slab foundation, please specify when ordering

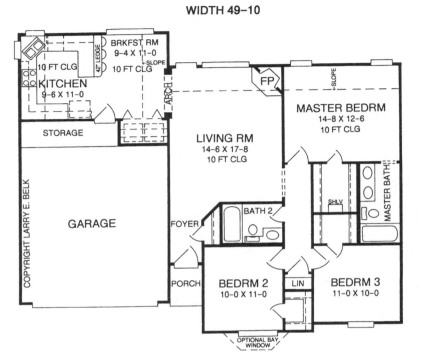

WIDTH 49–10

DEPTH 40–6

BRKFST RM
9-4 X 11-0
10 FT CLG

KITCHEN
9-6 X 11-0

10 FT CLG

42" LEDGE

STORAGE

COPYRIGHT LARRY E. BELK

GARAGE

MASTER BEDRM
14-8 X 12-6
10 FT CLG

FP

LIVING RM
14-6 X 17-8
10 FT CLG

MASTER BATH

SHLV

FOYER

BATH 2

PORCH

BEDRM 2
10-0 X 11-0

LIN

BEDRM 3
11-0 X 10-0

OPTIONAL BAY
WINDOW

Plan #X26-GSD-1001

Angled Den
With Built-Ins

Special features

- 3,158 total square feet of living area
- Coffered ceiling in entry
- Vaulted ceilings in living room, master bedroom and family room
- Interior columns accent the entry, living and dining areas
- Kitchen island has eating bar adding extra seating
- Master bath has garden tub and a separate shower
- 3 bedrooms, 2 1/2 baths, 3-car garage
- Crawl space foundation

TO ORDER SEE PAGE 320 OR CALL TOLL-FREE 1-800-DREAM HOME (373-2646)   33

Traditional Style With Extras

Special features

- 1,425 total square feet of living area
- Living room has very interesting cathedral ceiling
- Secondary bedrooms have plenty of closet space
- Raised eating counter separates kitchen and dining areas
- Bedroom #3 has seated window overlooking landscape
- 3 bedrooms, 2 baths, 2-car garage
- Basement foundation

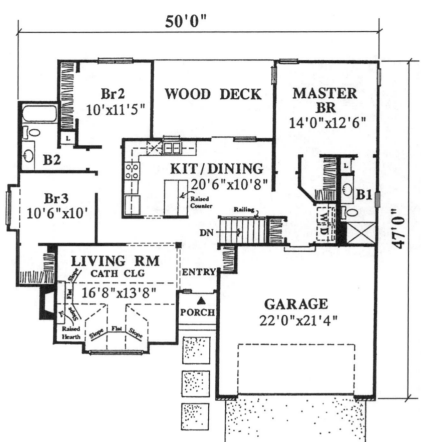

© COPYRIGHT 1990
RALPH JONES

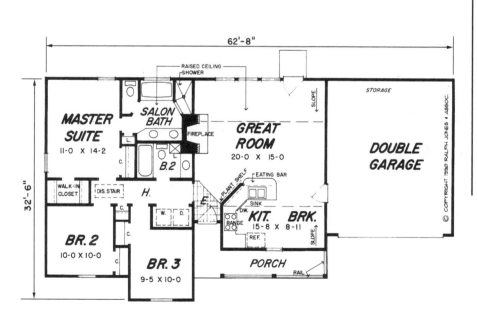

62'-8"

RAISED CEILING
SHOWER

MASTER SUITE
11-0 X 14-2

SALON BATH

B.2

GREAT ROOM
20-0 X 15-0

FIREPLACE

SLOPE

STORAGE

DOUBLE GARAGE

© COPYRIGHT 1990 RALPH JONES + ASSOC.

WALK-IN CLOSET

DIS. STAIR

H.

C.

C.

PLANT SHELF

EATING BAR

E

32'-6"

BR. 2
10-0 X 10-0

W. D.

C.

SINK

DW.

RANGE

REF.

KIT.
15-8 X 8-11

BRK.

SLOPE

BR. 3
9-5 X 10-0

PORCH

RAIL

Modest Ranch Style

Special features

- 1,192 total square feet of living area
- Kitchen eating bar overlooks well-designed great room
- Private bath in master suite
- Extra storage space in garage
- 3 bedrooms, 2 baths, 2-car garage
- Slab or crawl space foundation, please specify when ordering

Lovely, Spacious Floor Plan

Special features

- 1,558 total square feet of living area
- Spacious utility room located conveniently between garage and kitchen/dining area
- Private bedrooms separated off main living area by hallway
- Enormous living area with fireplace and vaulted ceiling opens to kitchen and dining area
- Master suite enhanced with large bay window, walk-in closet and private bath
- 3 bedrooms, 2 baths, 2-car garage
- Basement foundation

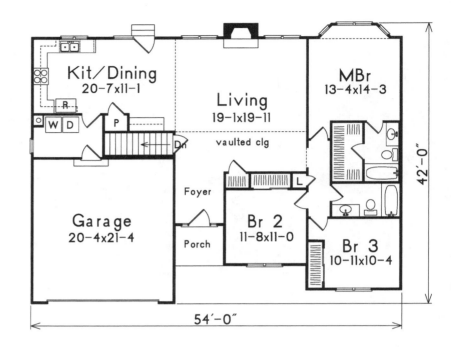

© Michael E. Nelson
NELSON DESIGN GROUP, LLC

Spacious Family Plan

Special features

- 2,092 total square feet of living area
- Master bedroom has private luxury bath
- Kitchen and breakfast room are centrally located
- Study/library is secluded from living areas
- 3 bedrooms, 2 baths, 2-car side entry garage
- Slab or crawl space foundation, please specify when ordering

Second Floor

©Alan Mascord Design Associates, Inc.

BR. 3
11/0 X 10/8

BR. 2
11/0 X 10/0

SHELVES

DN

LOFT

FOYER
BELOW

©Alan Mascord Design Associates, Inc.

LIN

LIVING
BELOW

VAULTED
MASTER
15/2 X 12/0

First Floor

©Alan Mascord Design Associates, Inc.

OPT. FR.
DRS.

DW
15/0 X 9/0

REF

PAN

DINING
10/6 X 12/0+

DN

UP

DN

NOOK
13/10 X 8/4

2 STORY
LIVING
13/0 X 14/0

FAMILY
13/10 X 20/8

35'

DECK

◄ 38' ►

Three-Story Design
Special features

- 1,978 total square feet of living area
- Designed for a sloping lot, this multi-level home intrigues the eye
- Sunlight filters into the grand two-story foyer and living room from tall windows
- Master suite has elegant front facing windows and a private bath
- 3 bedrooms, 2 1/2 baths, 2-car drive-under garage
- Walk-out basement foundation
- 1,106 square feet on the first floor and 872 square feet on the second floor

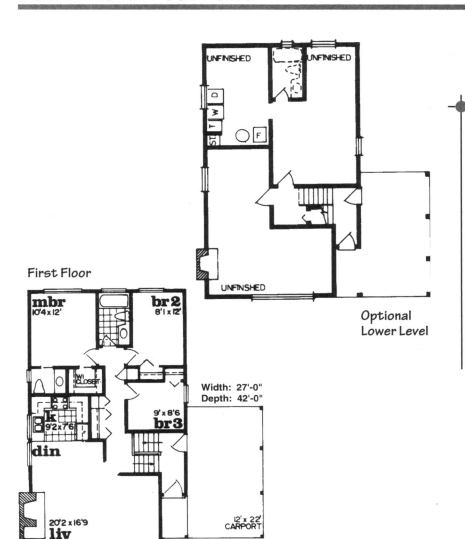

Optional
Lower Level

First Floor

Width: 27'-0"
Depth: 42'-0"

Rustic Home With Room To Grow

Special features

- 1,018 total square feet of living area
- Living room enjoys a corner fireplace and a large picture window
- U-shaped compact kitchen offers efficiency
- A half bath is situated in the master bedroom for convenience
- 1,018 square feet of optional living area available on the lower level
- 3 bedrooms, 1 1/2 baths, 1-car carport
- Basement foundation

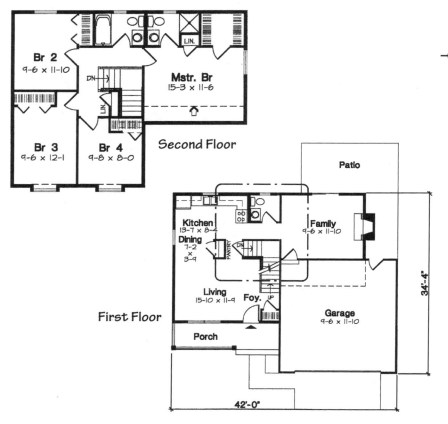

Br 2
9-6 x 11-10

Mstr. Br
15-3 x 11-6

Br 3
9-6 x 12-1

Br 4
9-8 x 8-0

DN

LIN.

Second Floor

Patio

Kitchen
13-7 x 8-4

Dining
7-2
x
3-9

PANTRY

DN

Family
9-6 x 11-10

Living
15-10 x 11-9

Foy.

UP

Garage
9-6 x 11-10

First Floor

Porch

34'-4"

42'-0"

Family Room Has Cozy Fireplace

Special features

- 1,505 total square feet of living area
- Spacious living room opens into the dining area which flows into an efficient kitchen
- All bedrooms located on the second floor for privacy
- Master suite has a large walk-in closet and a private bath with step-in shower
- 4 bedrooms, 2 1/2 baths, 2-car garage
- Basement, crawl space or slab foundation, please specify when ordering
- 692 square feet on the first floor and 813 square feet on the second floor

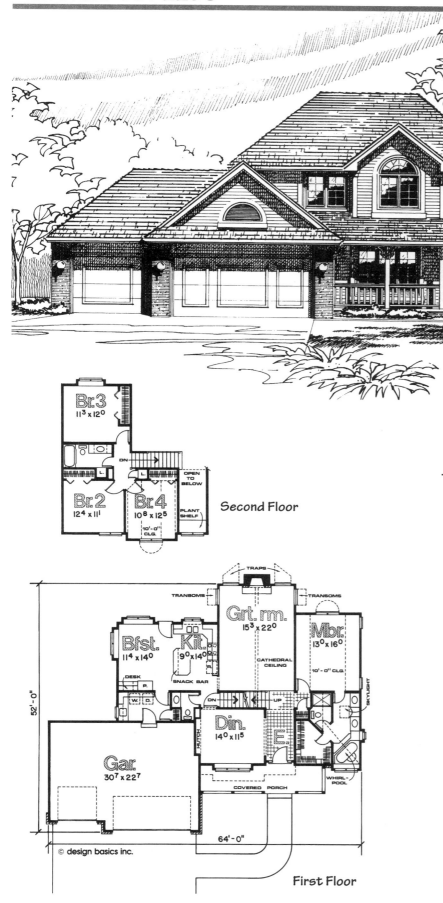

Second Floor

Br. 3
11^3 x 12^0

Br. 2
12^4 x 11^1

Br. 4
10^8 x 12^5

OPEN TO BELOW

PLANT SHELF

DN

L. L.

$10'$-$0''$ CLG.

First Floor

TRAPS

TRANSOMS   TRANSOMS

Grt. rm.
15^3 x 22^0

CATHEDRAL CEILING

Bfst.
11^4 x 14^0

Kit.
9^0 x 14^0

Mbr.
13^0 x 16^0

$10'$-$0''$ CLG.

DESK

P.

SNACK BAR

W.   D.

DN   UP

Din.
14^0 x 11^5

SKYLIGHT

Gar.
30^7 x 22^7

WHIRL-POOL

COVERED PORCH

$52'$-$0''$

$64'$-$0''$

© design basics inc.

Windows
Frame Fireplace

Special features

- 2,115 total square feet of living area
- Cathedral ceiling in great room adds spaciousness
- Two-story foyer is a grand entrance
- Efficiently designed kitchen with breakfast area, snack bar and built-in desk
- 4 bedrooms, 2 1/2 baths, 3-car garage
- Basement foundation
- 1,505 square feet on the first floor and 610 square feet on the second floor

Plenty Of Built-Ins

Special features

- 3,012 total square feet of living area
- Master suite has sitting area with entertainment center/library
- Utility room has a sink and includes lots of storage and counterspace
- Future space above garage has an additional 336 square feet of living area and its own stairway
- 4 bedrooms, 3 1/2 baths, 2-car side entry garage
- Crawl space, slab or basement foundation, please specify when ordering
- 2,202 square feet on the first floor and 810 square feet on the second floor

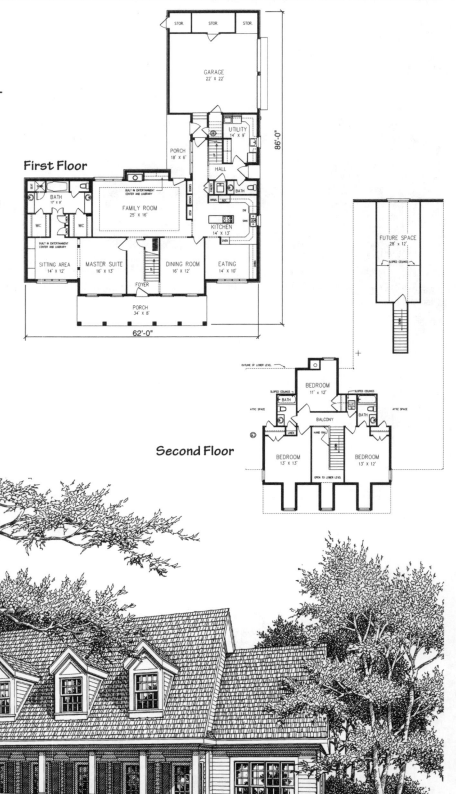

First Floor

Second Floor

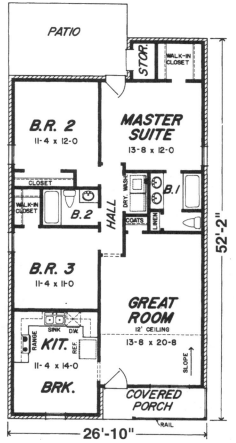

PATIO

STOR.

WALK-IN CLOSET

B.R. 2
11-4 x 12-0

MASTER SUITE
13-8 x 12-0

CLOSET

DRY. WASH.

B.1

WALK-IN CLOSET

B.2

HALL

COATS

LINEN

B.R. 3
11-4 x 11-0

52'-2"

GREAT ROOM
12' CEILING
13-8 x 20-8

RANGE

SINK   D.W.

REF.

KIT.
11-4 x 14-0

SLOPE

BRK.

COVERED PORCH

RAIL

26'-10"

Ranch With A Cottage Feel

Special features

- 1,253 total square feet of living area
- Compact kitchen with convenient breakfast room nearby
- 12' ceiling in great room adds a spacious feel
- Two secondary bedrooms share a hall bath
- Laundry closet located near all bedrooms
- 3 bedrooms, 2 baths
- Slab foundation

Wood Accents This Traditional Brick Home

Special features

- 1,404 total square feet of living area
- Living room, with bay window and fireplace, adjoins dining room
- Kitchen has an abundance of counter and cabinet space
- Two secondary bedroom share a full bath
- 3 bedrooms, 2 baths, 2-car garage
- Basement foundation

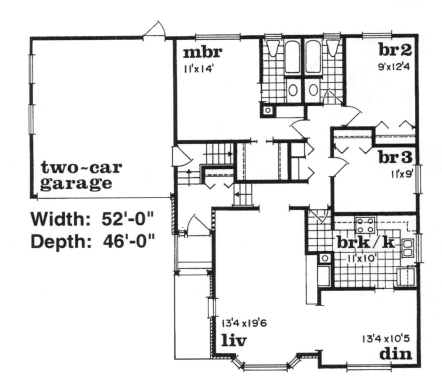

Width: 52'-0"
Depth: 46'-0"

Open Ranch Design Gives Expansive Look

Special features

- 1,630 total square feet of living area
- Crisp facade and full windows front and back offer open viewing
- Wrap-around rear deck is accessible from breakfast room, dining room and master bedroom
- Vaulted ceiling in living room and master bedroom
- Sitting area and large walk-in closet complement master bedroom
- Master bedroom has a private sitting area
- 3 bedrooms, 2 baths, 2-car garage
- Basement foundation

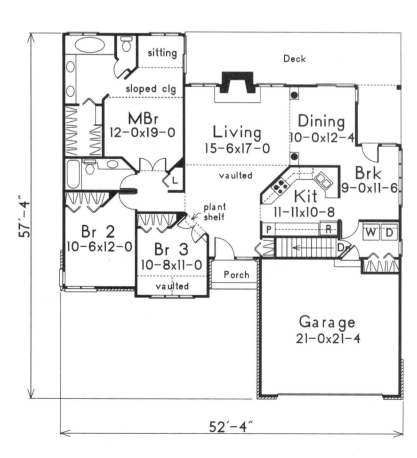

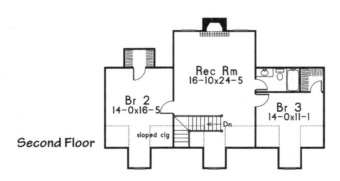

Second Floor

Rec Rm
16-10x24-5

Br 2
14-0x16-5

Br 3
14-0x11-1

sloped clg

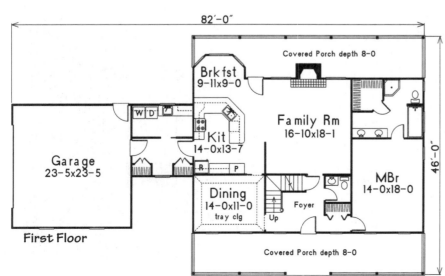

First Floor

82'-0"

46'-0"

Covered Porch depth 8-0

Brk fst
9-11x9-0

W D

Kit
14-0x13-7

Family Rm
16-10x18-1

Garage
23-5x23-5

Dining
14-0x11-0
tray clg

Foyer

Up

MBr
14-0x18-0

Covered Porch depth 8-0

Plenty Of Seating At Breakfast Bar

Special features

- 2,544 total square feet of living area
- Central family room becomes gathering place
- Second floor recreation room is a great game room for children
- First floor master suite secluded from main living areas
- 3 bedrooms, 2 1/2 baths, 2-car side entry garage
- Basement foundation, drawings also include crawl space and slab foundations
- 1,593 square feet on the first floor and 951 square feet on the second floor

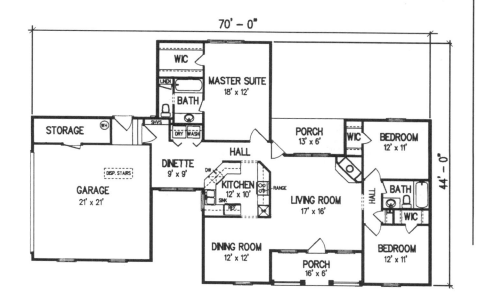

70' - 0"

44' - 0"

WIC

MASTER SUITE
18' x 12'

LINEN

BATH

SHVS

STORAGE

WH

DRY WASH

DINETTE
9' x 9'

HALL

DISP. STAIRS

GARAGE
21' x 21'

KITCHEN
12' x 10'

DW

SINK

RANGE

REF

PORCH
13' x 6'

WIC

BEDROOM
12' x 11'

LIVING ROOM
17' x 16'

HALL

BATH

WIC

DINING ROOM
12' x 12'

PORCH
16' x 6'

BEDROOM
12' x 11'

Comfortable Dinette

Special features

- 1,434 total square feet of living area
- Isolated master suite for privacy includes walk-in closet and bath
- Elegant formal dining room
- Efficient kitchen has an adjacent dinette which includes shelves and access to laundry facilities
- Extra storage in garage
- 3 bedrooms, 2 baths, 2-car side entry garage
- Crawl space or slab foundation, please specify when ordering

Traditional Styling Combines Brick And Siding

Special features

- 1,802 total square feet of living area

- Massive storage area at rear of garage could easily be converted to a work-shop

- Classic foyer leads to large great room with cathedral ceiling and centered fireplace

- Master bath features double vanity and separate shower and tub

- 3 bedrooms, 2 baths, 2-car garage

- Basement foundation

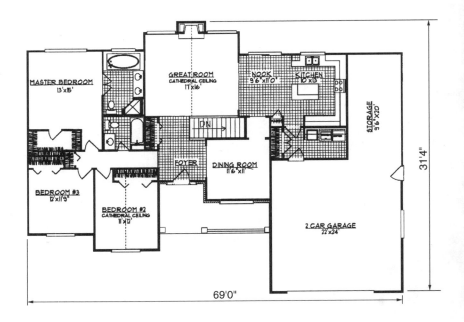

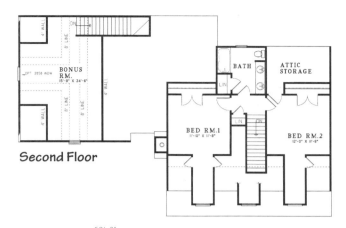

Second Floor

First Floor

Dormers Add Charm

Special features

- 2,107 total square feet of living area
- Kitchen has pantry and adjacent dining area
- Master bedroom with bath and large walk-in closet
- Second floor bedrooms have attic storage
- Rear stairs open into bonus room
- 3 bedrooms, 2 1/2 baths, 2-car garage
- Walk-out basement, basement, crawl space or slab foundation, please specify when ordering
- 1,124 square feet on the first floor and 983 square feet on the second floor

Second Floor Bonus Space

Special features

- 2,551 total square feet of living area
- Archway joins formal living room and family rooms
- Master suite has private bath and access to a covered patio
- Breakfast nook overlooks family room with cozy corner fireplace
- Optional living area over garage has an additional 287 square feet of living area
- 3 bedrooms, 3 baths, 2-car side entry garage
- Slab foundation

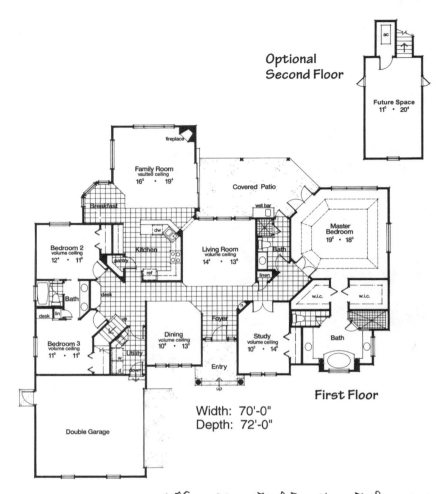

Optional Second Floor

Future Space
11⁰ · 20⁴

Family Room
vaulted ceiling
16⁶ · 19⁴

fireplace

Covered Patio

Breakfast

wet bar

dw

Kitchen

Living Room
volume ceiling
14⁴ · 13⁶

Master Bedroom
19² · 18⁰

Bath

Bedroom 2
volume ceiling
12⁴ · 11⁰

pantry

ref

linen

Bath

desk

w.i.c.

w.i.c.

desk   lin

Dining
volume ceiling
10⁸ · 13⁰

Foyer

Study
volume ceiling
10⁰ · 14⁴

Bath

Bedroom 3
volume ceiling
11⁰ · 11⁰

up

Utility

w

Entry

d   down

up

Double Garage

First Floor

Width: 70'-0"
Depth: 72'-0"

J. W. Hansen

A Charming Home Loaded With Extras

Special features

- 1,997 total square feet of living area

- Screened porch leads to a rear terrace with access to the breakfast room

- Living and dining rooms combine adding spaciousness to the floor plan

- Other welcome amenities include boxed windows in breakfast and dining rooms, a fireplace in living room and a pass-through snack bar in the kitchen

- 3 bedrooms, 2 1/2 baths

- Basement foundation

- 1,111 square feet on the first floor and 886 square feet on the second floor

Second Floor

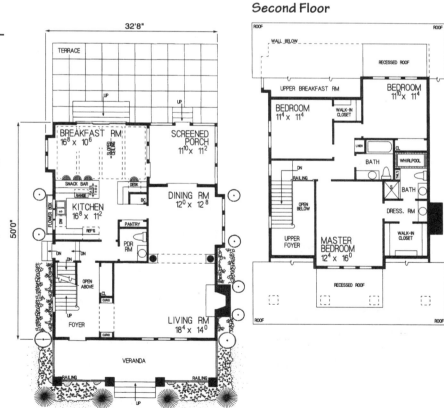

First Floor

Whirlpool With Skylight Above

Special features

- 1,911 total square feet of living area
- Large entry opens into beautiful great room with angled see-through fireplace
- Terrific design includes kitchen/ breakfast area with adjacent sunny bayed hearth room
- Luxury master suite has privacy from other bedrooms
- 3 bedrooms, 2 baths, 2-car garage
- Basement foundation

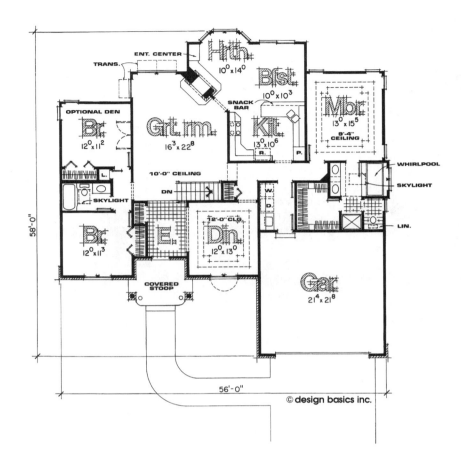

Chalet Cottage

Special features

- 1,073 total square feet of living area
- The front-facing deck and covered balcony add to outdoor living areas
- The fireplace is the main focus in the living room, separating the living room from the dining room
- Three large storage areas are found on the second floor
- 3 bedrooms, 1 1/2 baths
- Basement or crawl space foundation, please specify when ordering
- 672 square feet on the first floor and 401 square feet on the second floor

Width: 24'-0"
Depth: 36'-0"

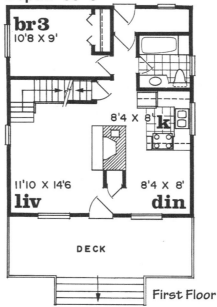

br3
10'8 X 9'

k
8'4 X 8'

liv
11'10 X 14'6

din
8'4 X 8'

DECK

First Floor

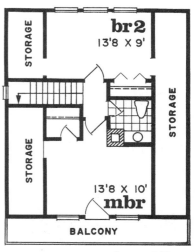

STORAGE

br2
13'8 X 9'

STORAGE

STORAGE

13'8 X 10'
mbr

BALCONY

Second Floor

Excellent Ranch For Country Setting

Special features

- 2,758 total square feet of living area
- Vaulted great room excels with fireplace, wet bar, plant shelves and skylights
- Fabulous master suite enjoys a fireplace, large bath, walk-in closet and vaulted ceiling
- Trendsetting kitchen/breakfast room adjoins spacious screened porch
- Convenient office near kitchen is perfect for computer room, hobby enthusiast or fifth bedroom
- 4 bedrooms, 2 1/2 baths, 3-car side entry garage
- Basement foundation

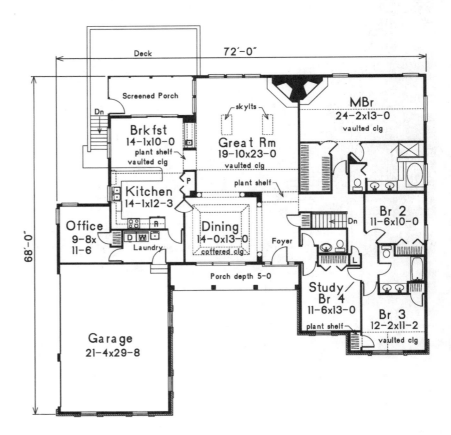

Master Suite
With Media Center

Special features

- 1,429 total square feet of living area
- Master suite with sitting area and private bath includes double walk-in closets
- Kitchen and dining area overlooks living room
- Living room has fireplace, media center and access to covered porch
- 3 bedrooms, 2 baths, 2-car garage
- Slab or crawl space foundation, please specify when ordering

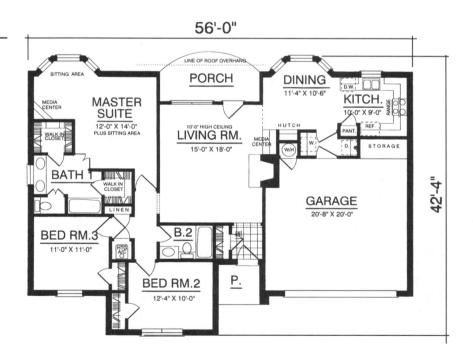

Elegant Barrier-Free Design

Special features

- 1,785 total square feet of living area
- Vaulted foyer opens to the living room which features a graceful archway framed by decorative columns and overhead plant shelves
- Bayed dining room also features an 11' ceiling and a French door that opens to a covered patio
- Open floor plan allows this home to be wheelchair accessible
- 3 bedrooms, 2 baths, 2-car garage
- Basement, crawl space or slab foundation, please specify when ordering

Width: 58'-0"
Depth: 57'-0"

Vaulted Ceilings Enhance Spacious Home

Special features

- 2,073 total square feet of living area
- Family room provides ideal gathering area with a fireplace, large windows and vaulted ceiling
- Private first floor master bedroom suite with a vaulted ceiling and luxury bath
- Kitchen features angled bar connecting kitchen and breakfast area
- 4 bedrooms, 2 1/2 baths, 2-car side entry garage
- Basement foundation
- 1,441 square feet on the first floor and 632 square feet on the second floor

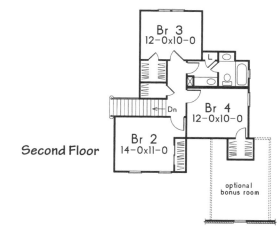

Second Floor

Br 3
12-0x10-0

Br 4
12-0x10-0

Br 2
14-0x11-0

optional bonus room

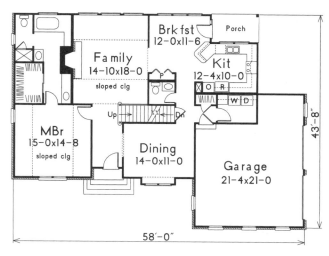

First Floor

Brk fst
12-0x11-6

Porch

Family
14-10x18-0
sloped clg

Kit
12-4x10-0

MBr
15-0x14-8
sloped clg

Dining
14-0x11-0

Garage
21-4x21-0

43'-8"

58'-0"

Enchanting Country Cottage

Special features

- 1,140 total square feet of living area
- Open and spacious living and dining areas for family gatherings
- Well-organized kitchen with an abundance of cabinetry and a built-in pantry
- Roomy master bath features double-bowl vanity
- 3 bedrooms, 2 baths, 2-car drive under garage
- Basement foundation

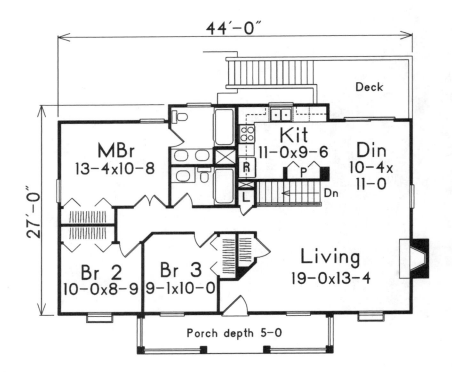

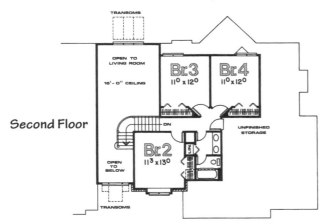

Second Floor

OPEN TO LIVING ROOM
15'-0" CEILING

Br. 3
11⁰ x 12⁰

Br. 4
11⁰ x 12⁰

DN

UNFINISHED STORAGE

Br. 2
11³ x 13⁰

OPEN TO BELOW

TRANSOMS

Unique Entry
Special features
- 2,486 total square feet of living area
- Cozy gathering room off breakfast/ kitchen area is a great entertaining area
- Den has pocket door entrance into master suite making an ideal retreat or home office
- Master suite has all the amenities like walk-in closet, whirlpool tub and raised ceiling
- 4 bedrooms, 2 1/2 baths, 3-car garage
- Basement foundation
- 1,829 square feet on the first floor and 657 square feet on the second floor

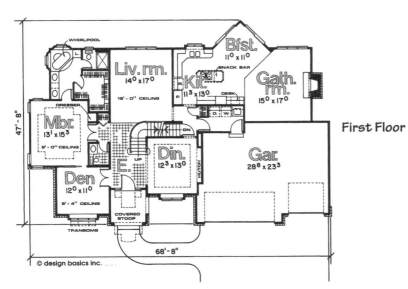

WHIRLPOOL

Liv. rm.
14' x 17⁰
15'-0" CEILING

Bfst.
11⁰ x 11⁰

SNACK BAR

Kit.
11³ x 13⁰

DESK

Gath. rm.
15⁰ x 17⁰

D.W.

Mbr.
13¹ x 15³
9'-0" CEILING

Din.
12³ x 13⁰

Gar.
28⁸ x 23³

UP

DN

Den
12⁰ x 11⁰
9'-4" CEILING

COVERED STOOP

TRANSOMS

First Floor

47'-8"

68'-8"

© design basics inc.

Comfortable Living In This Ranch

Special features

- 1,379 total square feet of living area
- Vaulted great room makes a lasting impression with corner fireplace and windows
- Formal dining room easily connects to kitchen making entertaining easy
- Master bath includes all the luxuries such as a spacious walk-in closet, oversized tub and separate shower
- 3 bedrooms, 2 baths, 2-car garage
- Slab foundation

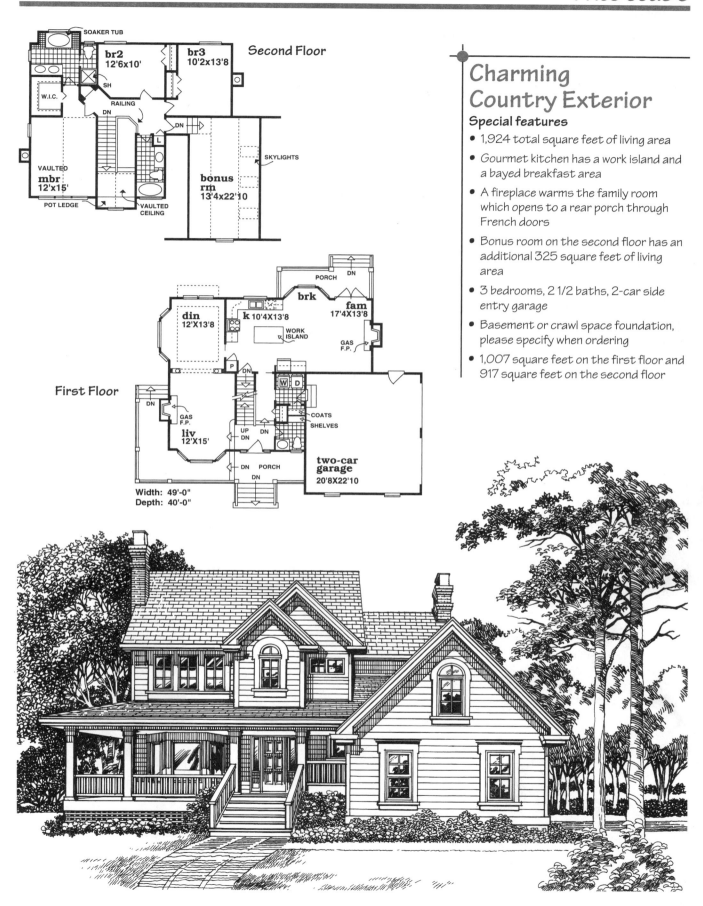

Second Floor

SOAKER TUB

br2
12'6x10'

br3
10'2x13'8

W.I.C.

SH

RAILING

DN

DN

L

SKYLIGHTS

VAULTED
mbr
12'x15'

bonus
rm
13'4x22'10

POT LEDGE

VAULTED
CEILING

First Floor

PORCH

DN

din
12'X13'8

brk

k 10'4X13'8

fam
17'4X13'8

WORK
ISLAND

GAS
F.P.

P

DN

W D

GAS
F.P.

DN

liv
12'X15'

COATS

SHELVES

UP
DN

DN

two-car
garage
20'8X22'10

DN PORCH
DN

Width: 49'-0"
Depth: 40'-0"

Charming
Country Exterior
Special features

- 1,924 total square feet of living area
- Gourmet kitchen has a work island and a bayed breakfast area
- A fireplace warms the family room which opens to a rear porch through French doors
- Bonus room on the second floor has an additional 325 square feet of living area
- 3 bedrooms, 2 1/2 baths, 2-car side entry garage
- Basement or crawl space foundation, please specify when ordering
- 1,007 square feet on the first floor and 917 square feet on the second floor

Built-In Computer Desk

Special features

- 1,525 total square feet of living area
- Corner fireplace highlighted in great room
- Unique glass block window over whirlpool tub in master bath
- Open bar overlooks both the kitchen and great room
- Breakfast room leads to outdoor grilling and covered porch
- 3 bedrooms, 2 baths, 2-car garage
- Basement, walk-out basement, crawl space or slab foundation, please specify when ordering

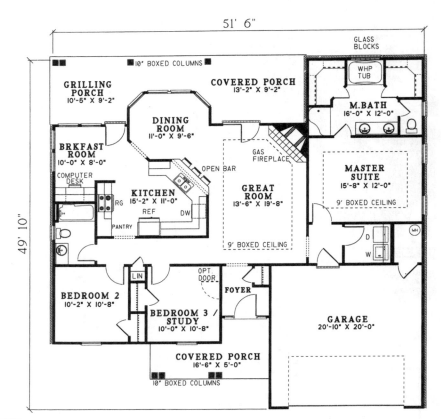

Second Floor

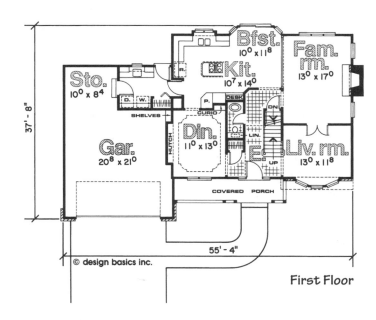

First Floor

Large Utility Room

Special features

- 1,998 total square feet of living area
- Lovely designed family room offers double-door entrance into living area
- Roomy kitchen with breakfast area is a natural gathering place
- 10' ceiling in master bedroom
- 3 bedrooms, 2 1/2 baths, 2-car garage
- Basement foundation
- 1,093 square feet on the first floor and 905 square feet on the second floor

Distinctive Country Porch

Special features

- 2,182 total square feet of living area
- Meandering porch creates an inviting look
- Generous great room has four double-hung windows and gliding doors to exterior
- Highly functional kitchen features island/breakfast bar, menu-desk and convenient pantry
- Each secondary bedroom includes generous closetspace and a private bath
- 3 bedrooms, 3 1/2 baths, 2-car side entry garage
- Basement foundation, drawings also include crawl space and slab foundations
- 1,112 square feet on the first floor and 1,070 square feet on the second floor

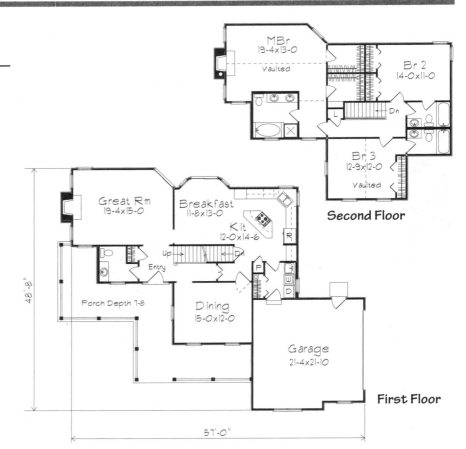

Second Floor

First Floor

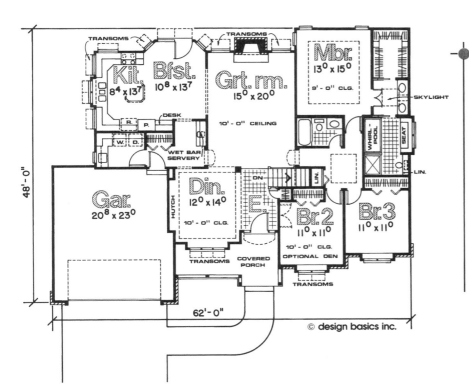

Convenient Wet Bar

Special features

- 1,850 total square feet of living area
- Oversized rooms throughout
- Great room spotlights fireplace with sunny windows on both sides
- Master bedroom has private skylighted bath
- Interesting wet bar between kitchen and dining area is an added bonus when entertaining
- 3 bedrooms, 2 baths, 2-car garage
- Basement foundation

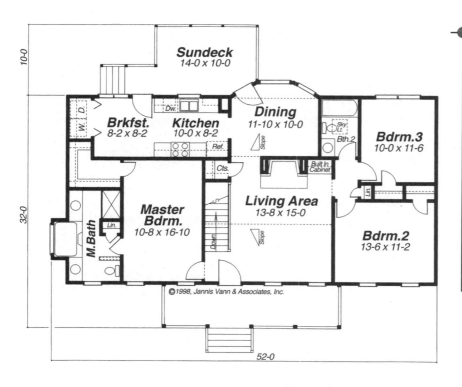

Sundeck
14-0 x 10-0

Brkfst.
8-2 x 8-2

Kitchen
10-0 x 8-2

Dining
11-10 x 10-0

Dw.

Ref.

Slope

Cts.

W. D.

Sky. Lt.

Bth.2

Built In. Cabinet

Bdrm.3
10-0 x 11-6

Lin.

Master Bdrm.
10-8 x 16-10

Living Area
13-8 x 15-0

Slope

Down

M. Bath

Lin.

Bdrm.2
13-6 x 11-2

© 1998, Jannis Vann & Associates, Inc.

10-0

32-0

52-0

Formal Country Charm

Special features

- 1,325 total square feet of living area

- Sloped ceiling and a fireplace in living area creates a cozy feeling

- Formal dining and breakfast areas have an efficiently designed kitchen between them

- Master bedroom has walk-in closet with luxurious private bath

- 3 bedrooms, 2 baths, 2-car drive under garage

- Basement foundation

WIDTH 65–10

DEPTH 53–5

MASTER BATH

PORCH

BRKFST RM
10-8 X 11-8
10 FT CLG

UTIL
8-0 X 5-8

STORAGE

STORAGE

MASTER BEDRM
14-4 X 15-6
10 FT CLG

FP

LIVING ROOM
17-4 X 15-8
10 FT CLG

KITCHEN
10-8 X 13-6
10 FT CLG

GARAGE

COPYRIGHT LARRY E. BELK

PAN

BATH 2

LIN

BEDROOM 2
12-6 X 11-6

BEDROOM 3
12-0 X 13-4
10 FT CLG

FOYER
10 FT CLG

DINING ROOM
11-0 X 13-0
10 FT COFFERED CLG

PORCH

Formal Facade

Special features

- 1,890 total square feet of living area
- 10' ceilings give this home a spacious feel
- Efficient kitchen has breakfast bar which overlooks living room
- Master bedroom has private bath with walk-in closet
- 3 bedrooms, 2 baths, 2-car side entry garage
- Crawl space or slab foundation, please specify when ordering

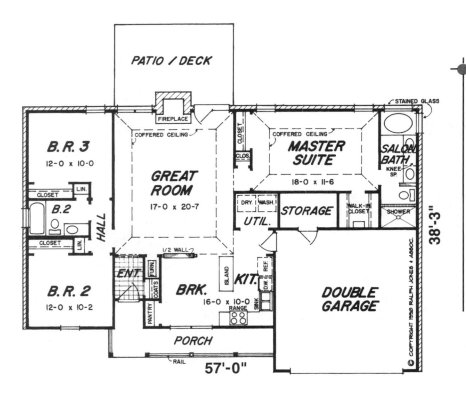

Cozy Country Appeal

Special features

- 1,482 total square feet of living area
- Coffered ceiling in master suite adds a dramatic feel
- Half-wall in breakfast room helps maintain an open flowing floor plan
- Covered front porch creates a place for a quiet retreat
- 3 bedrooms, 2 baths, 2-car garage
- Slab or crawl space foundation, please specify when ordering

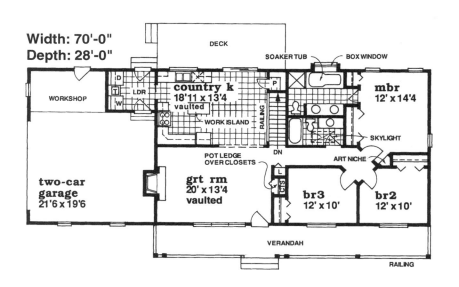

Width: 70'-0"
Depth: 28'-0"

DECK

SOAKER TUB   BOX WINDOW

WORKSHOP

D
T   LDR
W

country k
18'11 x 13'4
vaulted

WORK ISLAND

P

mbr
12' x 14'4

RAILING

DN

SKYLIGHT

ART NICHE

POT LEDGE
OVER CLOSETS

two-car
garage
21'6 x 19'6

grt rm
20' x 13'4
vaulted

L
CTS

br3
12' x 10'

br2
12' x 10'

VERANDAH

RAILING

Vaulted Ceilings Add A Sense Of Spaciousness

Special features

- 1,408 total square feet of living area
- A bright country kitchen boasts an abundance of counterspace and cupboards
- The front entry is sheltered by a broad verandah
- A spa tub is brightened by a box bay window in the master bath
- 3 bedrooms, 2 baths, 2-car side entry garage
- Basement or crawl space foundation, please specify when ordering

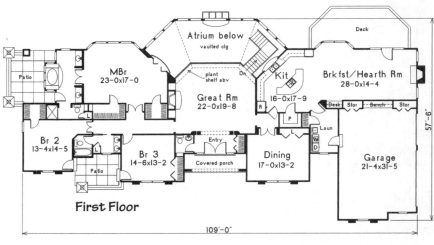

First Floor

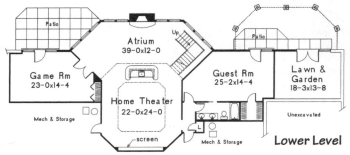

Lower Level

A Spectacular Showplace

Special features

- 4,826 total square feet of living area
- Brightly lit entry connects to great room with balcony and massive bay-shaped atrium
- Kitchen has island/snack bar, walk-in pantry, computer area and atrium overlook
- Master suite has sitting area, walk-in closets, atrium overlook and luxury bath with private courtyard
- Family room/atrium, home theater area with wet bar, game room and guest bedroom comprise the lower level
- 4 bedrooms, 3 1/2 baths, 3-car side entry garage
- Walk-out basement foundation with lawn and garden workroom
- 3,050 square feet on the first floor and 1,776 square feet on the lower level

Great Room/Atrium Interior View

Second Floor

PLAYROOM
17'-4" X 17'-0"

GREAT ROOM BELOW

BEDR'M 2
12'-0" X 11'-0"

CL

BEDR'M-3
17'-0" X 11'-0"

CL

BATH-2

CL

DN

BALCONY

FOYER BELOW

First Floor

DOUBLE GARAGE
20'-0" X 20'-0"

UTIL
F W D

STOR

MASTER SUITE
17'-0" X 15'-0"

GREAT ROOM
15'-0" X 20'-0"

1/2 BATH

NICHE

HEARTH ROOM
20'-0" X 13'-0"

F/P

F/P

MASTER BATH

KIT

NICHE REF

DW
S

BRK
10'-0" X 10'-0"

W.I.C.

GALLERY

DINING
11'-0" X 15'-0"

SU

FOYER

PANT

PORCH

63'-0"

65'-0"

Grand Covered Entry

Special features

- 3,369 total square feet of living area
- Large playroom overlooks to great room below and makes a great casual family area
- Extra storage is located in garage
- Well-planned hearth room and kitchen are open and airy
- Foyer flows into unique diagonal gallery area creating a dramatic entrance into the great room
- 3 bedrooms, 2 1/2 baths, 2-car side entry garage
- Walk-out basement foundation
- 2,154 square feet on the first floor and 1,215 square feet on the second floor

Extra Large Porches

Special features

- 1,716 total square feet of living area

- Great room boasts a fireplace and access to the kitchen/breakfast area through a large arched opening

- Master bedroom includes a huge walk-in closet and French doors that lead onto an L-shaped porch

- Bedrooms #2 and #3 share a bath and linen closet

- 3 bedrooms, 2 baths, 2-car detached garage

- Crawl space or slab foundation, please specify when ordering

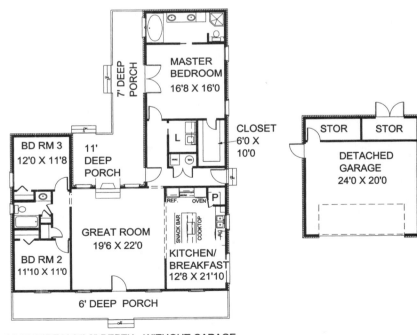

7' DEEP PORCH

MASTER BEDROOM
16'8 X 16'0

CLOSET
6'0 X 10'0

BD RM 3
12'0 X 11'8

11' DEEP PORCH

L

BD RM 2
11'10 X 11'0

GREAT ROOM
19'6 X 22'0

REF. OVEN P

SNACK BAR COOKTOP

KITCHEN/ BREAKFAST
12'8 X 21'10

6' DEEP PORCH

44'-0" WIDE X 65'-0" DEPTH - WITHOUT GARAGE

STOR STOR

DETACHED GARAGE
24'0 X 20'0

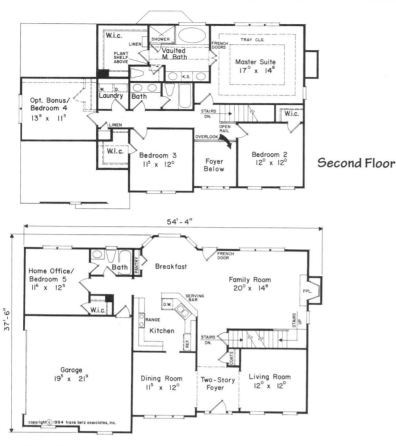

Second Floor

First Floor

Open Family Living
Special features

- 2,352 total square feet of living area
- All bedrooms on second floor for privacy
- Kitchen and breakfast area flow into family room with fireplace
- Two-story foyer is open and airy
- Optional bonus room has an additional 168 square feet of living area
- 4 bedrooms, 3 baths, 2-car side entry garage
- Walk-out basement or crawl space foundation, please specify when ordering
- 1,294 square feet on the first floor and 1,058 square feet on the second floor

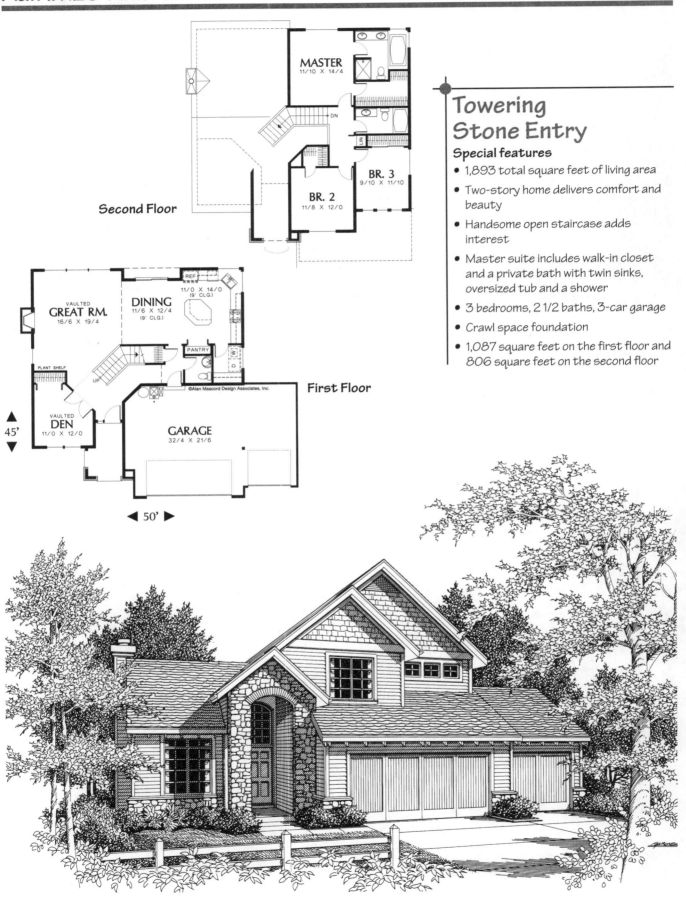

Second Floor

MASTER
11/10 X 14/4

BR. 3
9/10 X 11/10

BR. 2
11/8 X 12/0

First Floor

VAULTED
GREAT RM.
16/6 X 19/4

DINING
11/6 X 12/4
(9' CLG.)

11/0 X 14/0
(9' CLG.)

REF

PANTRY

PLANT SHELF

UP

VAULTED
DEN
11/0 X 12/0

45'

©Alan Mascord Design Associates, Inc.

GARAGE
32/4 X 21/6

50'

Towering Stone Entry

Special features

- 1,893 total square feet of living area
- Two-story home delivers comfort and beauty
- Handsome open staircase adds interest
- Master suite includes walk-in closet and a private bath with twin sinks, oversized tub and a shower
- 3 bedrooms, 2 1/2 baths, 3-car garage
- Crawl space foundation
- 1,087 square feet on the first floor and 806 square feet on the second floor

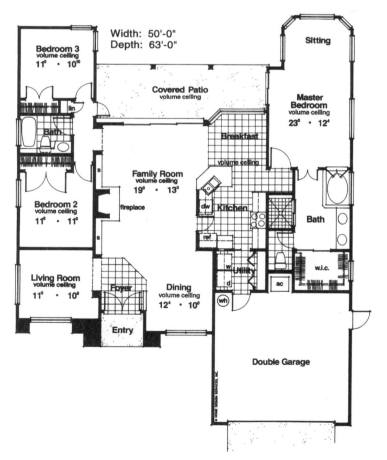

Width: 50'-0"
Depth: 63'-0"

Bedroom 3
volume ceiling
11⁰ · 10¹⁰

Sitting

Covered Patio
volume ceiling

Master
Bedroom
volume ceiling
23⁰ · 12⁴

Breakfast

volume ceiling

Bath

lin

Family Room
volume ceiling
19⁰ · 13⁰

Kitchen

Bedroom 2
volume ceiling
11⁰ · 11⁰

fireplace

dw

ref

Bath

w
Utility
d

w.i.c.

Living Room
volume ceiling
11⁰ · 10⁸

Foyer

Dining
volume ceiling
12⁴ · 10⁰

ac

wh

Entry

Double Garage

Impressive Entry

Special features

- 1,817 total square feet of living area
- Master suite has its own sitting area flooded with sunlight
- Family room has fireplace flanked by bookshelves
- Open and airy dining room flows into the family room
- 3 bedrooms, 2 baths, 2-car garage
- Slab foundation

Open Living Areas Separate Remote Bedrooms

Special features

- 1,868 total square feet of living area
- Luxurious master bath is impressive with angled quarter-circle tub, separate vanities and large walk-in closet
- Energy efficient home with 2" x 6" exterior walls
- Dining room is surrounded by series of arched openings which complement the open feeling of this design
- Living room has a 12' ceiling accented by skylights and a large fireplace flanked by sliding doors
- Large storage areas
- 3 bedrooms, 2 baths, 2-car side entry garage
- Slab foundation, drawings also include crawl space foundation

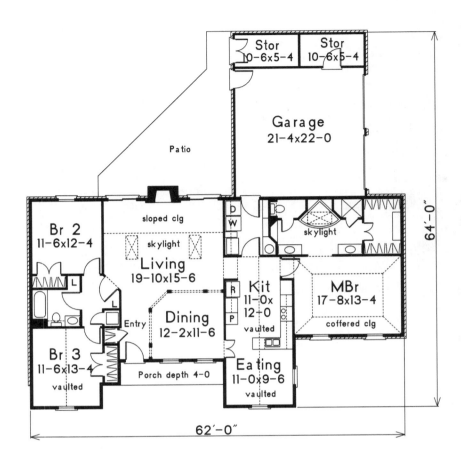

Formal And Informal Living

Special features

- 2,591 total square feet of living area
- Formal living area has a nice view extending past the covered patio
- Family room is adjacent to breakfast area and has vaulted ceiling and fireplace creating a cozy atmosphere
- Master suite has a private sitting area
- 4 bedrooms, 3 baths, 3-car side entry garage
- Slab foundation

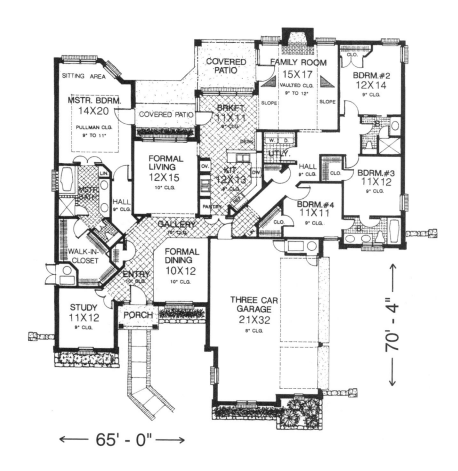

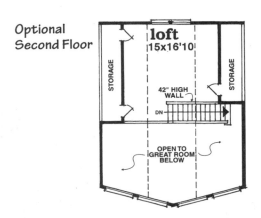

Optional Second Floor

loft
15x16'10

STORAGE

STORAGE

42" HIGH WALL

DN

OPEN TO GREAT ROOM BELOW

Spectacular Views From Expansive Window Wall

Special features

- 1,375 total square feet of living area
- Open U-shaped kitchen shares an eating bar with the dining room
- Two secondary bedrooms share a full bath
- Master suite provides a walk-in closet and private bath
- 284 square feet of optional living area on the second floor
- 3 bedrooms, 2 baths
- Basement or crawl space foundation, please specify when ordering

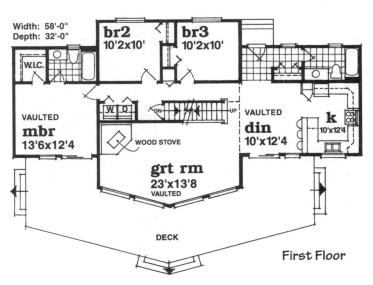

Width: 58'-0"
Depth: 32'-0"

br2
10'2x10'

br3
10'2x10'

W.I.C.

VAULTED
mbr
13'6x12'4

W D

DN

UP

VAULTED
din
10'x12'4

k
10'x12'4

WOOD STOVE

grt rm
23'x13'8
VAULTED

DECK

First Floor

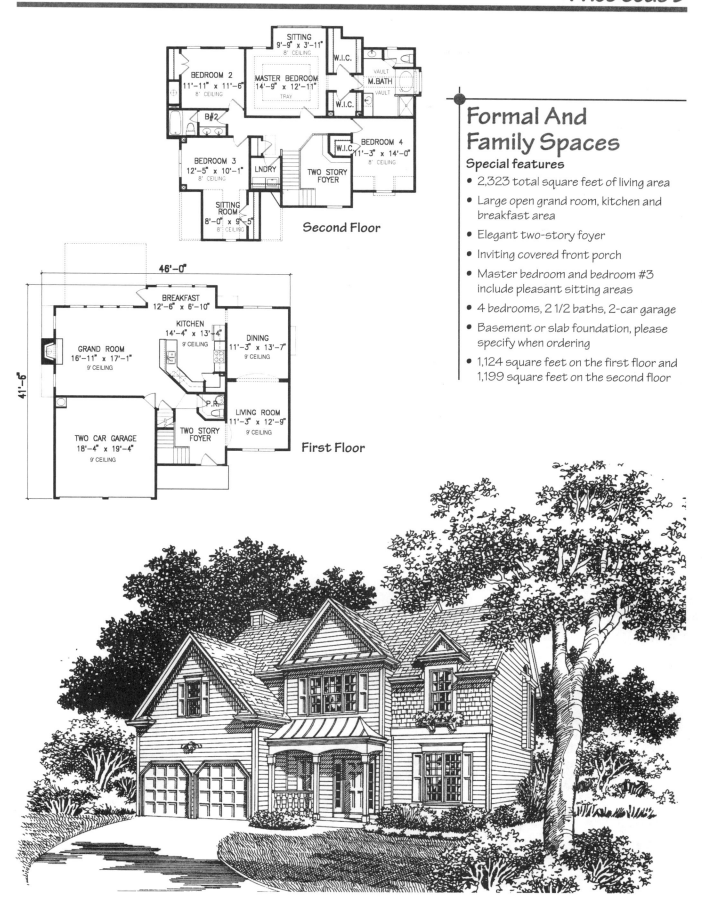

Second Floor

SITTING
9'-9" x 3'-11"
8' CEILING

BEDROOM 2
11'-11" x 11'-6"
8' CEILING

MASTER BEDROOM
14'-9" x 12'-11"
TRAY

W.I.C.

VAULT
M.BATH
VAULT

B#2

BEDROOM 3
12'-5" x 10'-1"
8' CEILING

LNDRY

TWO STORY
FOYER

W.I.C.

BEDROOM 4
11'-3" x 14'-0"
8' CEILING

SITTING
ROOM
8'-0" x 9'-5"
8' CEILING

First Floor

46'-0"

41'-6"

BREAKFAST
12'-6" x 6'-10"

KITCHEN
14'-4" x 13'-4"
9' CEILING

DINING
11'-3" x 13'-7"
9' CEILING

GRAND ROOM
16'-11" x 17'-1"
9' CEILING

P.R.

LIVING ROOM
11'-3" x 12'-9"
9' CEILING

TWO CAR GARAGE
18'-4" x 19'-4"
9' CEILING

TWO STORY
FOYER

Formal And Family Spaces

Special features

- 2,323 total square feet of living area
- Large open grand room, kitchen and breakfast area
- Elegant two-story foyer
- Inviting covered front porch
- Master bedroom and bedroom #3 include pleasant sitting areas
- 4 bedrooms, 2 1/2 baths, 2-car garage
- Basement or slab foundation, please specify when ordering
- 1,124 square feet on the first floor and 1,199 square feet on the second floor

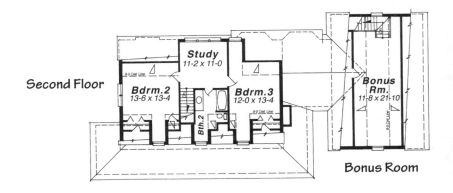

Second Floor

Bonus Room

Open Floor Plan With Plenty Of Light

Special features

- 2,475 total square feet of living area
- Country feeling with wrap-around porch and dormered front
- Open floor plan with living and dining areas combined has access to a sun deck
- First floor master bedroom with many luxuries
- 3 bedrooms, 2 1/2 baths, 2-car side entry garage
- Walk-out basement foundation
- 1,362 square feet on the first floor, 729 square feet on the second floor and 384 square feet in the bonus room

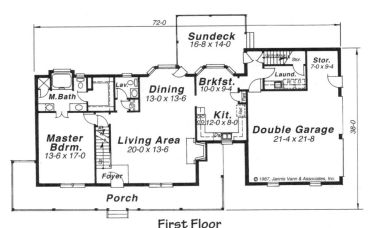

First Floor

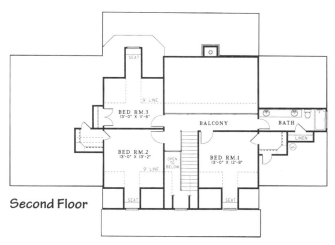

Second Floor

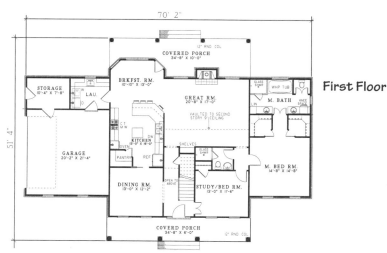

First Floor

Cozy Covered Porches

Special features

- 2,698 total square feet of living area
- Great room feels spacious with vaulted ceiling and windows overlooking covered porch
- Master suite bath has a glass shower and whirlpool tub
- Laundry area includes counterspace and sink
- 4 bedrooms, 3 baths, 2-car side entry garage
- Basement, walk-out basement, crawl space or slab foundation, please specify when ordering
- 1,813 square feet on the first floor and 885 square feet on the second floor

6' HIGH WOOD PRIVACY FENCE

BATH
CLO.
SHV
LINEN
VANITY

MASTER SUITE
15' x 14'

LIN

BED RM.
13' x 12'
CLO.
CLO.

PORCH
10' x 10'

DINING
12' x 10'

LIN

BATH
HALL
CLO.

LIVING
18' x 16'

BAR
SINK
D.W.
KITCHEN
12' x 10'
RANGE   REF

CLO.
WASH
UTIL
8' x 6'
DRY

STOR
12' x 5'

56'

BED RM.
13' x 12'
CLO.
SLOPE   CEILING

PORCH
12' x 6'

HEAT
& AC
WH

ATTIC
STAIRS

GARAGE
22' x 21'

52'

Central Living Room

Special features

- 1,420 total square feet of living area
- Energy efficient home has 2" x 6" exterior walls
- Living room has 12' ceiling, corner fireplace and atrium doors leading to covered porch
- Separate master suite has garden bath and walk-in closet
- 3 bedrooms, 2 baths, 2-car garage
- Slab or crawl space foundation, please specify when ordering

K.KAUSS

TO ORDER SEE PAGE 320 OR CALL TOLL-FREE 1-800-DREAM HOME (373-2646)

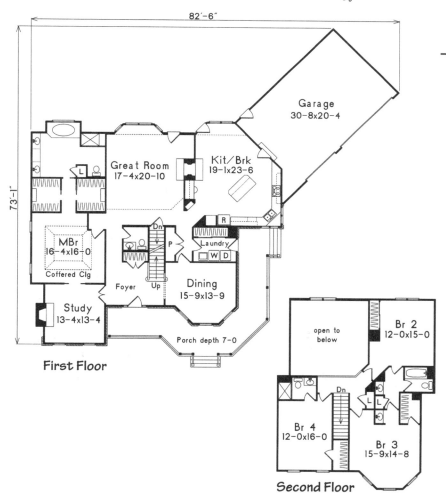

First Floor

- 82'-6"
- 73'-1"
- Garage 30-8x20-4
- Great Room 17-4x20-10
- Kit/Brk 19-1x23-6
- MBr 16-4x16-0 Coffered Clg
- Laundry
- W D
- P
- R
- Dn
- Up
- Foyer
- Dining 15-9x13-9
- Study 13-4x13-4
- Porch depth 7-0

Second Floor

- open to below
- Br 2 12-0x15-0
- Br 4 12-0x16-0
- Br 3 15-9x14-8
- Dn

Wrap-Around Porch And Turret Accent Design

Special features

- 3,556 total square feet of living area
- Jack and jill bath located between two of the bedrooms on the second floor
- Second floor features three bedrooms and overlooks the great room
- Formal entrance and additional family entrance from covered porch to laundry/mud room
- First floor master suite features coffered ceiling, his and hers walk-in closets, luxury bath and direct access to study
- 4 bedrooms, 3 1/2 baths, 3-car side entry garage
- Basement foundation
- 2,212 square feet on the first floor and 1,344 square feet on the second floor

Second Floor

First Floor

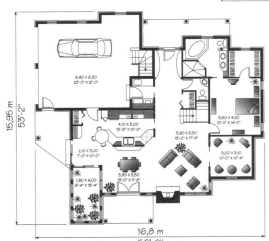

Perfect Home For Seaside, Lake Or Mountain Views

Special features

- 1,995 total square feet of living area
- First floor solarium creates a sunny atmosphere
- Second floor office is tucked away from traffic areas for privacy
- Energy efficient home with 2" x 6" exterior walls
- 3 bedrooms, 2 1/2 baths, 2-car side entry garage
- Basement foundation
- 1,525 square feet on the first floor and 470 square feet on the second floor

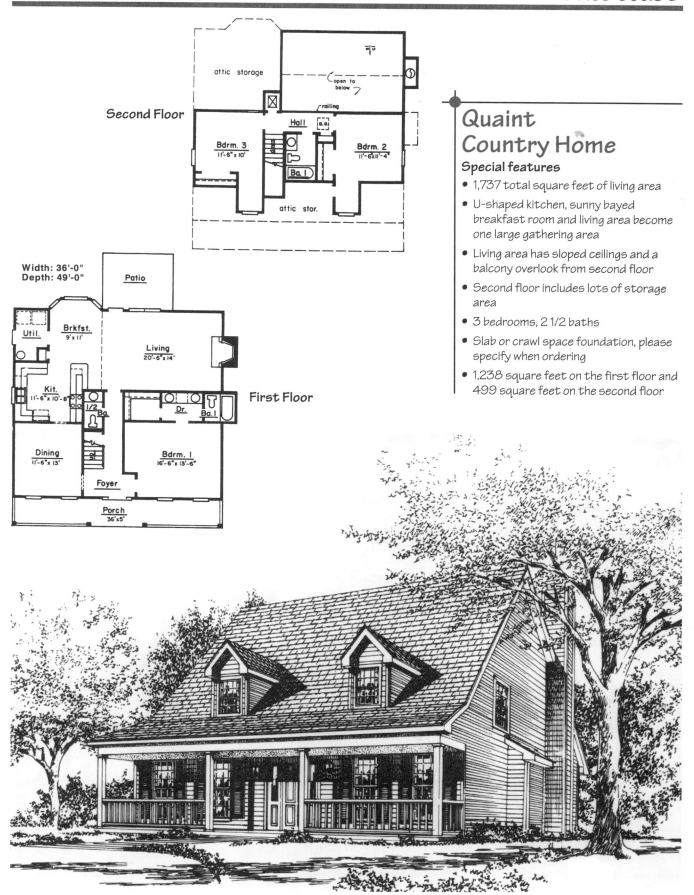

Second Floor

attic storage

open to below

railing

Hall

Bdrm. 3
11'-6" x 10'

Ba 1

Bdrm. 2
11'-6"x 11'-4"

attic stor.

Width: 36'-0"
Depth: 49'-0"

Patio

Util.

Brkfst.
9' x 11'

Living
20'-6" x 14'

Kit.
11'-6" x 10'-8"

1/2 Ba

Dr.

Ba. 1

First Floor

Dining
11'-6" x 13'

Bdrm. 1
16'-6" x 13'-6"

Foyer

Porch
36'x 5'

Quaint Country Home
Special features

- 1,737 total square feet of living area
- U-shaped kitchen, sunny bayed breakfast room and living area become one large gathering area
- Living area has sloped ceilings and a balcony overlook from second floor
- Second floor includes lots of storage area
- 3 bedrooms, 2 1/2 baths
- Slab or crawl space foundation, please specify when ordering
- 1,238 square feet on the first floor and 499 square feet on the second floor

A Vacation Home For All Seasons

Special features

- 1,039 total square feet of living area
- Cathedral construction provides the maximum in living area openness
- Expansive glass viewing walls
- Two decks, front and back
- Charming second story loft arrangement
- Simple, low-maintenance construction
- 2 bedrooms, 1 1/2 baths
- Crawl space foundation
- 764 square feet on the first floor and 275 square feet on the second floor

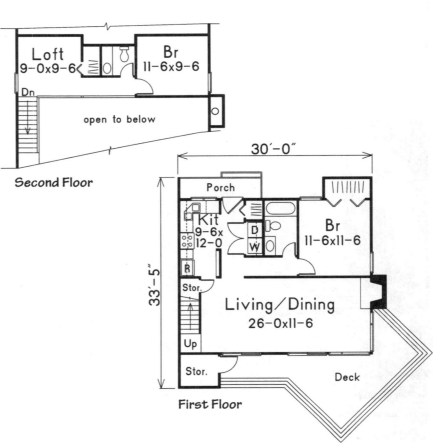

Second Floor

Loft
9-0x9-6

Br
11-6x9-6

Dn

open to below

30'-0"

33'-5"

Porch

Kit
9-6x
12-0

Br
11-6x11-6

D
W

R

Stor.

Up

Stor.

Living/Dining
26-0x11-6

Deck

First Floor

Sunny Dining Room

Special features

- 1,735 total square feet of living area
- Luxurious master bath has spa tub, shower, double vanity and large walk-in closet
- Peninsula in kitchen has sink and dishwasher
- Massive master bedroom has step up ceiling and private location
- 3 bedrooms, 2 baths, 2-car garage
- Slab foundation

Width: 50'-0"
Depth: 55'-0"

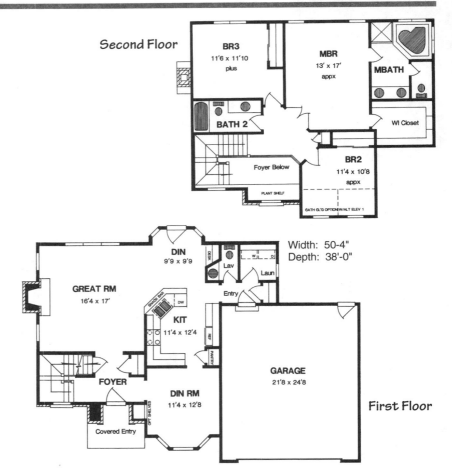

Second Floor

BR3
11'6 x 11'10
plus

MBR
13' x 17'
appx

MBATH

BATH 2

WI Closet

Foyer Below

PLANT SHELF

BR2
11'4 x 10'8
appx

CATH CL'G OPTION W/ALT ELEV 1

Traditional Styling

Special features

- 1,873 total square feet of living area

- Formal dining area in the front of the house is conveniently located near kitchen

- Large great room has fireplace and lots of windows

- Master bedroom has double-door entry with a private bath

- 3 bedrooms, 2 1/2 baths, 2-car garage

- Basement foundation

- 931 square feet on the first floor and 942 square feet on the second floor

DIN
9'9 x 9'9

Width: 50'-4"
Depth: 38'-0"

GREAT RM
16'4 x 17'

Lav

Laun

Entry

KIT
11'4 x 12'4

SNACK BAR

DW

PANTRY

GARAGE
21'8 x 24'8

FOYER

DIN RM
11'4 x 12'8

OPT SHELVES

Covered Entry

First Floor

C. Kowalski

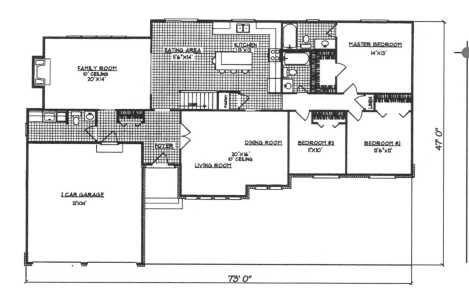

Transsoms
Brighten Facade

Special features

- 2,042 total square feet of living area
- Dining and living rooms joined for large formal gatherings
- Family room with tall ceiling and fireplace is secluded for casual enjoyment
- 3 bedrooms, 2 1/2 baths, 2-car garage
- Basement foundation

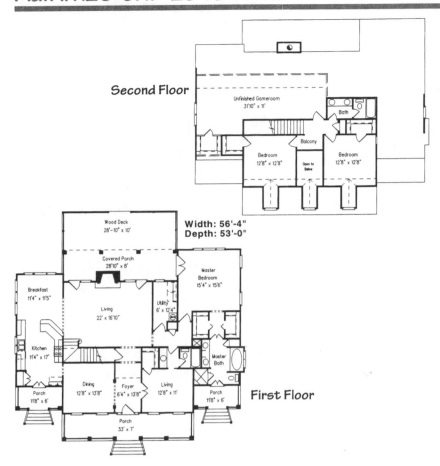

Second Floor

Unfinished Gameroom
31'10" x 11'

Bath

Balcony

Bedroom
12'8" x 12'8"

Open to Below

Bedroom
12'8" x 12'8"

Wood Deck
28'-10" x 10'

Width: 56'-4"
Depth: 53'-0"

Covered Porch
28'10" x 8'

Breakfast
11'4" x 11'5"

Living
22' x 16'10"

Utility
6' x 12'4"

Master
Bedroom
15'4" x 15'6"

Kitchen
11'4" x 17'

Master
Bath

Dining
12'8" x 13'8"

Foyer
6'4" x 13'8"

Living
12'8" x 11'

Porch
11'8" x 6'

Porch
11'8" x 6'

First Floor

Porch
33' x 7'

Porches Bring Outdoor Living In

Special features

- 2,500 total square feet of living area
- Master suite has its own separate wing with front porch, double walk-in closets, private bath and access to back porch and patio
- Large unfinished gameroom on second floor
- Living area is oversized and has a fireplace
- 3 bedrooms, 2 1/2 baths
- Basement, slab or crawl space foundation, please specify when ordering
- 1,910 square feet on the first floor and 590 square feet on the second floor

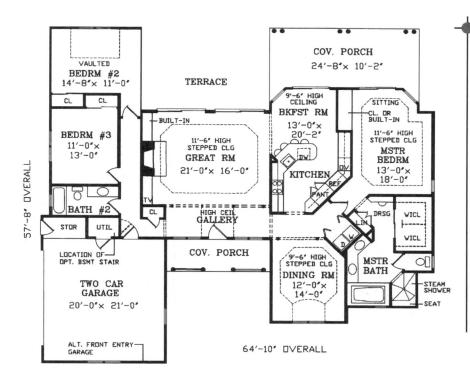

VAULTED BEDRM #2 14'-8" x 11'-0"

CL CL

BEDRM #3 11'-0" x 13'-0"

BATH #2

STOR UTIL

LOCATION OF OPT. BSMT STAIR

TWO CAR GARAGE 20'-0" x 21'-0"

ALT. FRONT ENTRY GARAGE

57'-8" OVERALL

TERRACE

BUILT-IN

11'-6" HIGH STEPPED CLG **GREAT RM** 21'-0" x 16'-0"

TV

CL

HIGH CEIL. **GALLERY**

COV. PORCH

COV. PORCH 24'-8" x 10'-2"

9'-6" HIGH CEILING **BKFST RM** 13'-0" x 20'-2"

KITCHEN

DW

REF

PANT

SITTING CL. OR BUILT-IN

11'-6" HIGH STEPPED CLG **MSTR BEDRM** 13'-0" x 18'-0"

DV

DRSG VICL

LIN VICL

9'-6" HIGH STEPPED CLG **DINING RM** 12'-0" x 14'-0"

MSTR BATH

STEAM SHOWER

SEAT

64'-10" OVERALL

Dramatic Angled Kitchen
Special features

- 2,018 total square feet of living area

- Large expanses of elegant curved transomed windows flank the beautiful entrance

- Great room includes French doors to a large covered rear porch

- Luxurious master suite has fabulous master bath, double closets and accesses rear porch

- 3 bedrooms, 2 baths, 2-car side entry garage

- Basement, slab or crawl space foundation, please specify when ordering

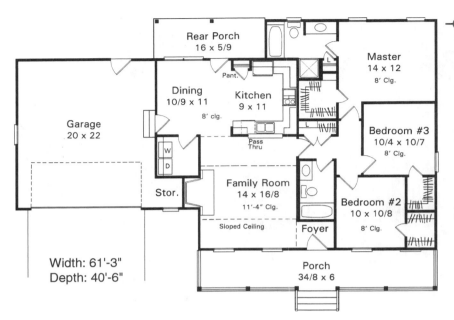

Rear Porch
16 x 5/9

Master
14 x 12
8' Clg.

Dining
10/9 x 11
8' clg.

Kitchen
9 x 11

Pant.

Garage
20 x 22

Pass
Thru

Bedroom #3
10/4 x 10/7
8' Clg.

W
D

Family Room
14 x 16/8
11'-4" Clg.

Bedroom #2
10 x 10/8
8' Clg.

Stor.

Sloped Ceiling

Foyer

Porch
34/8 x 6

Width: 61'-3"
Depth: 40'-6"

Covered Rear Porch
Special features
- 1,253 total square feet of living area
- Sloped ceiling and fireplace in family room adds drama
- U-shaped kitchen efficiently designed
- Large walk-in closets are found in all the bedrooms
- 3 bedrooms, 2 baths, 2-car garage
- Crawl space or slab foundation, please specify when ordering

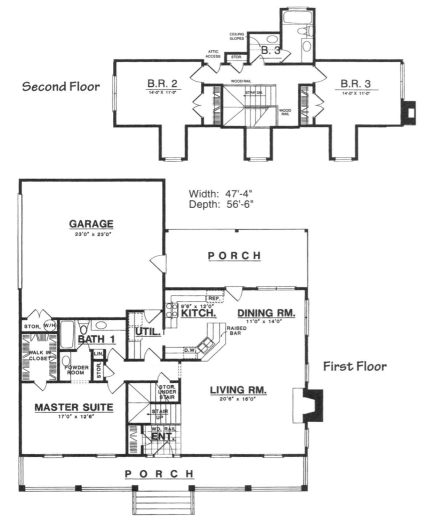

Second Floor

B.R. 2
14'-0" X 11'-0"

B.R. 3
14'-0" X 11'-0"

B. 3

CEILING SLOPES

ATTIC ACCESS

STOR.

WOOD RAIL

STAIR DN.

WOOD RAIL

First Floor

Width: 47'-4"
Depth: 56'-6"

GARAGE
23'0" x 23'0"

PORCH

REF.

KITCH.
9'6" x 12'0"

DINING RM.
11'0" x 14'0"

RAISED BAR

D.W.

UTIL.

STOR. W/H

BATH 1

WALK IN CLOSET

LIN.

POWDER ROOM

STOR.

STOR. UNDER STAIR

LIVING RM.
20'6" x 16'0"

STAIR UP

MASTER SUITE
17'0" x 12'8"

WD. RAIL

ENT.

PORCH

Kitchen Overlooks Living Area

Special features

- 1,815 total square feet of living area

- Well-designed kitchen opens to dining room and features raised breakfast bar

- First floor master suite has walk-in closet

- Front and back porches unite this home with the outdoors

- 3 bedrooms, 2 baths, 2-car side entry garage

- Basement, crawl space or slab foundation, please specify when ordering

- 1,245 square feet on the first floor and 570 square feet on the second floor

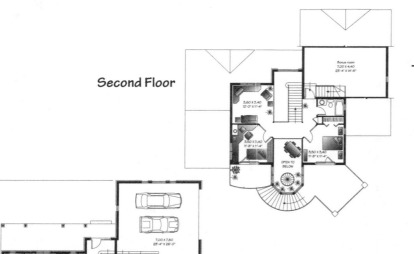

Second Floor

First Floor

Charming Two-Story

Special features

- 1,922 total square feet of living area
- Cathedral ceiling in bedroom 1 and in second floor solarium
- 9' ceilings throughout this home
- Energy efficient home with 2" x 6" exterior walls
- 3 bedrooms, 2 1/2 baths, 2-car side entry garage
- Partial basement/crawl space foundation
- 1,293 square feet on the first floor and 629 square feet on the second floor

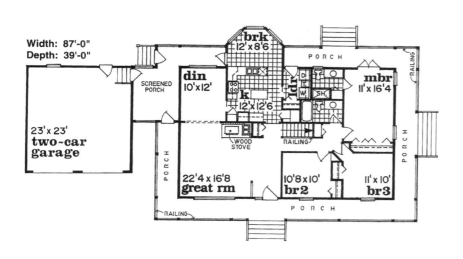

Width: 87'-0"
Depth: 39'-0"

SCREENED PORCH

23' x 23'
two~car garage

brk
12' x 8'6

din
10' x 12'

k

dr

D
T
W

SH

mbr
11' x 16'4

PORCH

RAILING

WOOD STOVE

RAILING

PORCH

22'4 x 16'8
great rm

10'8 x 10'
br2

11' x 10'
br3

PORCH

RAILING

PORCH

Country Ranch With Spacious Wrap-Around Porch

Special features

- 1,541 total square feet of living area
- Dining area offers access to a screened porch for outdoor dining and entertaining
- A country kitchen features a center island and a breakfast bay for casual meals
- Great room is warmed by a woodstove
- 3 bedrooms, 2 baths, 2-car garage
- Basement or crawl space foundation, please specify when ordering

Inviting
Covered Porch
And Angled Entry

Special features

- 2,534 total square feet of living area
- Den includes double-door entry off foyer and can serve as a guest suite with direct access to a 3/4 bath
- Island kitchen is equipped with an eating bar and desk
- 10' ceiling in living room
- 4 bedrooms, 3 baths, 3-car garage
- Basement foundation
- 1,511 square feet on the first floor and 1,023 square feet on the second floor

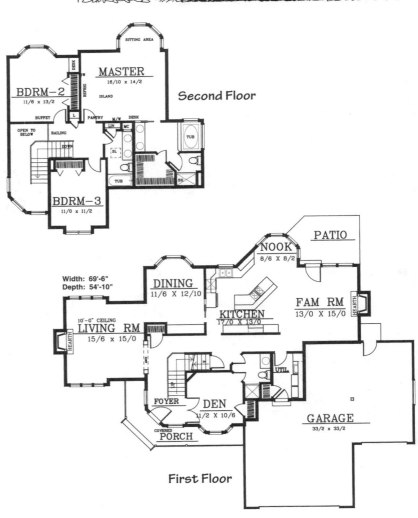

Second Floor

First Floor

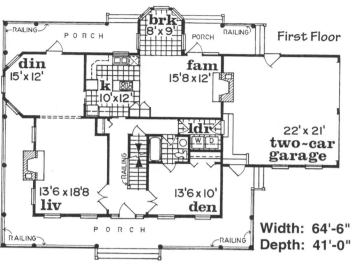

First Floor

brk
8' x 9'

din
15' x 12'

fam
15'8 x 12'

k
10' x 12'

ldr

22' x 21'
two~car
garage

13'6 x 18'8
liv

13'6 x 10'
den

PORCH

RAILING

W D

Width: 64'-6"
Depth: 41'-0"

Traditional Farmhouse Feeling With This Home

Special features

- 2,582 total square feet of living area
- Both the family and living rooms are warmed by hearths
- The master suite on the second floor has a bayed sitting room and a private bath with whirlpool tub
- Old-fashioned window seat in second floor landing is a charming touch
- 4 bedrooms, 3 baths, 2-car side entry garage
- Basement or crawl space foundation, please specify when ordering
- 1,291 square feet on the first floor and 1,291 square feet on the second floor

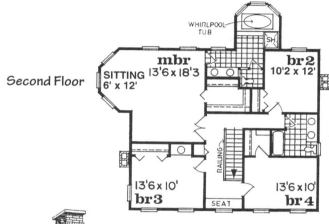

Second Floor

WHIRLPOOL TUB

SH

mbr
13'6 x 18'3

SITTING
6' x 12'

br2
10'2 x 12'

RAILING

13'6 x 10'
br3

SEAT

13'6 x 10'
br4

Simple Rooflines And Inviting Porch Enhance Design

Special features

- 1,389 total square feet of living area
- Formal living room has warming fireplace and a delightful bay window
- U-shaped kitchen shares a snack bar with the bayed family room
- Lovely master suite has its own private bath
- 3 bedrooms, 2 baths, 2-car garage
- Slab foundation

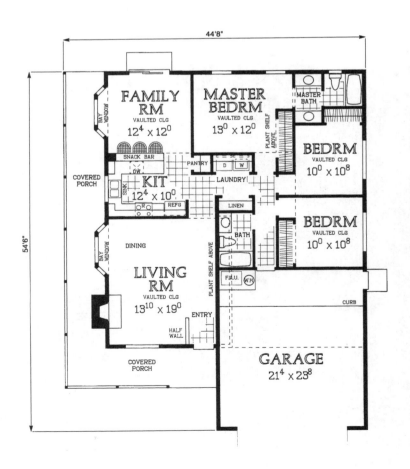

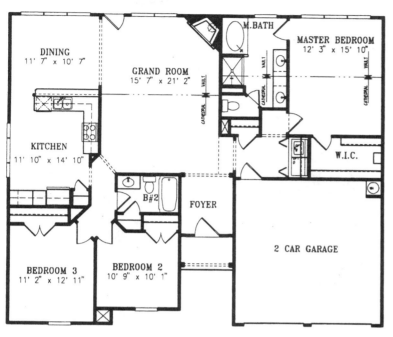

DINING
11' 7" x 10' 7"

GRAND ROOM
15' 7" x 21' 2"

M.BATH

MASTER BEDROOM
12' 3" x 15' 10"

KITCHEN
11' 10" x 14' 10"

W.I.C.

B#2

FOYER

2 CAR GARAGE

BEDROOM 3
11' 2" x 12' 11"

BEDROOM 2
10' 9" x 10' 1"

Width: 50'-0"
Depth: 42'-0"

Corner Fireplace In Grand Room

Special features

- 1,606 total square feet of living area
- Kitchen has snack bar which overlooks dining area for convenience
- Master bedroom has lots of windows with a private bath and large walk-in closet
- Cathedral vault in great room adds spaciousness
- 3 bedrooms, 2 baths, 2-car garage
- Slab foundation

HOLZHAUER INC. 93

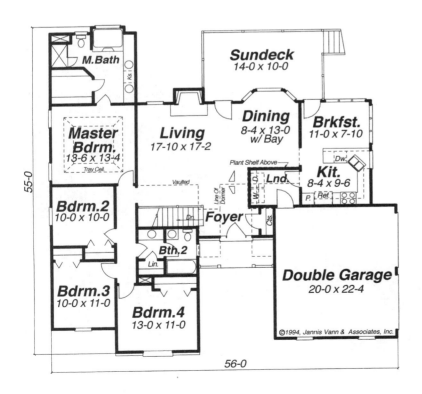

M.Bath

Sundeck
14-0 x 10-0

Master Bdrm.
13-6 x 13-4
Tray Ceil.

Living
17-10 x 17-2

Dining
8-4 x 13-0
w/ Bay

Brkfst.
11-0 x 7-10

Plant Shelf Above

Kit.
8-4 x 9-6

Lnd.

Vaulted

Bdrm.2
10-0 x 10-0

Foyer

Bth.2

Lin.

Bdrm.3
10-0 x 11-0

Bdrm.4
13-0 x 11-0

Double Garage
20-0 x 22-4

©1994, Jannis Vann & Associates, Inc.

55-0

56-0

Traditional And Country Styling

Special features

- 1,716 total square feet of living area

- Combination of stone and siding finish give home country feel

- Formal dining area has bay windows looking out to sun deck

- Master suite has private bath with large walk-in closet, double vanity, large tub and shower

- 4 bedrooms, 2 baths, 2-car side entry garage

- Basement foundation

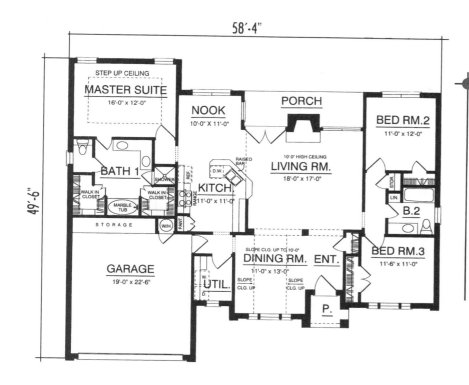

58'-4"

49'-6"

STEP UP CEILING

MASTER SUITE
16'-0" x 12'-0"

NOOK
10'-0" X 11'-0"

PORCH

BED RM.2
11'-0" x 12'-0"

BATH 1

SHOWER

D.W.

RAISED BAR

10'-0" HIGH CEILING
LIVING RM.
18'-0" x 17'-0"

STOR

WALK IN CLOSET

MARBLE TUB

WALK IN CLOSET

KITCH.
11'-0" x 11'-0"

REF.

RANGE

LIN.

B.2

STORAGE

W/H

PANT.

GARAGE
19'-0" x 22'-6"

W. D.

UTIL.

SLOPE CLG. UP TO 10'-0"
DINING RM.
11'-0" x 13'-0"

SLOPE CLG. UP

SLOPE CLG. UP

ENT.

BED RM.3
11'-6" x 11'-0"

P.

Attractive Styling

Special features

- 1,791 total square feet of living area
- Dining area has 10' high sloped ceiling
- Kitchen opens to large living room with fireplace and access onto a covered porch
- Master suite features private bath, double walk-in closets and whirlpool tub
- 3 bedrooms, 2 baths, 2-car garage
- Slab or crawl space foundation, please specify when ordering

Great Views
At Rear Of Home

Special features

- 2,197 total square feet of living area
- Centrally located great room opens to kitchen, breakfast nook and private backyard
- Den located off entry ideal for home office
- Vaulted master bath has spa tub, shower and double vanity
- 3 bedrooms, 2 1/2 baths, 2-car garage
- Crawl space foundation

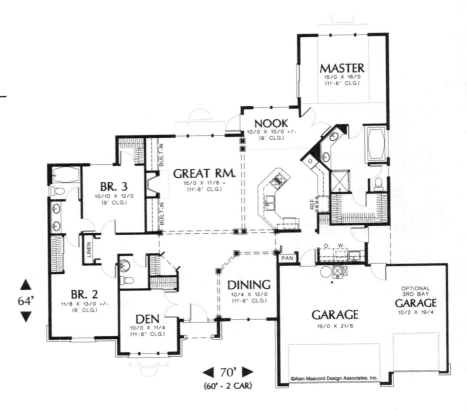

MASTER
15/0 X 16/0
(11'-6" CLG.)

NOOK
10/0 X 10/0 +/-
(9' CLG.)

GREAT RM.
15/0 X 17/6 +
(11'-6" CLG.)

BR. 3
10/10 X 12/0
(9' CLG.)

BR. 2
11/8 X 13/0 +/-
(9' CLG.)

DEN
10/0 X 11/4
(11'-6" CLG.)

DINING
10/4 X 12/0
(11'-6" CLG.)

PAN.

REF.

D.   W.

GARAGE
19/0 X 21/6

OPTIONAL
3RD BAY
GARAGE
10/2 X 19/4

LINEN

BUILT-IN

64'

◀ 70' ▶
(60' - 2 CAR)

©Alan Mascord Design Associates, Inc.

Second Floor

Br 2
12-11x12-7

open to below

Br 3
12-0x13-3

Dn

open to below

Br 4
12-1x12-4

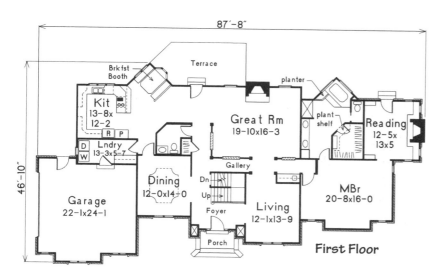

87'-8"

46'-10"

Brkfst Booth

Terrace

planter

Kit
13-8x
12-2

R P

D W

Lndry
13-3x5-7

Great Rm
19-10x16-3

plant shelf

Reading
12-5x
13x5

Gallery

Dining
12-0x14-0

Dn
Up

Foyer

Living
12-1x13-9

MBr
20-8x16-0

Garage
22-1x24-1

Porch

First Floor

Arched Elegance

Special features

- 3,222 total square feet of living area
- Two-story foyer features central staircase and views to second floor, dining and living rooms
- Built-in breakfast booth surrounded by windows
- Gourmet kitchen with view to the great room
- Two-story great room features large fireplace and arched openings to the second floor
- Elegant master suite has separate reading room with bookshelves and fireplace
- 4 bedrooms, 3 1/2 baths, 2-car side entry garage
- Basement foundation, drawings also include crawl space and slab foundations
- 2,276 square feet on the first floor and 946 square feet on the second floor

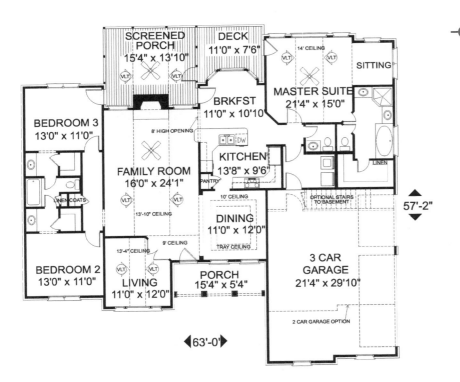

SCREENED PORCH
15'4" x 13'10"
VLT / VLT

DECK
11'0" x 7'6"
VLT

14' CEILING
VLT

SITTING

BEDROOM 3
13'0" x 11'0"

8' HIGH OPENING

BRKFST
11'0" x 10'10

MASTER SUITE
21'4" x 15'0"

FAMILY ROOM
16'0" x 24'1"
VLT / VLT

KITCHEN
13'8" x 9'6"
PANTRY

DW

LINEN

13'-10" CEILING

10' CEILING

LINEN COATS

DINING
11'0" x 12'0"

OPTIONAL STAIRS TO BASEMENT

TRAY CEILING

57'-2"

BEDROOM 2
13'0" x 11'0"

13'-4" CEILING
VLT / VLT

9' CEILING

LIVING
11'0" x 12'0"

PORCH
15'4" x 5'4"

3 CAR GARAGE
21'4" x 29'10"

2 CAR GARAGE OPTION

◄63'-0"►

Elegant Arched Front Porch Attracts Attention

Special features

- 1,992 total square feet of living area
- Bayed breakfast room overlooks outdoor deck and connects to screened porch
- Private formal living room in the front of the home could easily be converted to a home office or study
- Compact, yet efficient kitchen is conveniently situated between the breakfast and dining rooms
- 3 bedrooms, 2 1/2 baths, 3-car side entry garage
- Basement, crawl space or slab foundation, please specify when ordering

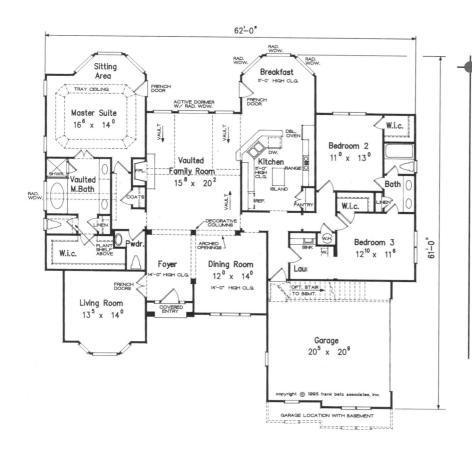

62'-0"

Sitting Area

TRAY CEILING

Master Suite
16⁶ x 14⁰

FRENCH DOOR

ACTIVE DORMER W/ RAD. WDW.

RAD. WDW.

Breakfast
11'-0" HIGH CLG.

RAD. WDW.

RAD. WDW.

FRENCH DOOR

W.i.c.

Bedroom 2
11⁰ x 13⁰

VAULT

VAULT

DBL. OVEN

SHWR.

Vaulted M.Bath

FPL.

Vaulted Family Room
15⁸ x 20²

Kitchen
11'-0' HIGH CLG.

DW.

ISLAND

RANGE

Bath

RAD. WDW.

COATS

VAULT

PANTRY

W.i.c.

LINEN

I.REF.

LINEN

W.i.c.

PLANT SHELF ABOVE

Pwdr.

DECORATIVE COLUMNS

ARCHED OPENINGS

W.H.

SINK

Bedroom 3
12¹⁰ x 11⁶

W.

Foyer
14'-0" HIGH CLG.

Dining Room
12⁰ x 14⁰
14'-0" HIGH CLG.

Laur.

FRENCH DOORS

COVERED ENTRY

OPT. STAIR TO BSMT.

Living Room
13⁵ x 14⁰

Garage
20⁵ x 20⁹

61'-0"

copyright © 1995 frank betz associates, inc.

GARAGE LOCATION WITH BASEMENT

Bounty Of Bay Windows

Special features

- 2,322 total square feet of living area
- Vaulted family room has fireplace and access to kitchen
- Decorative columns and arched openings surround dining area
- Master suite has a sitting room and grand scale bath
- Kitchen includes island with serving bar
- 3 bedrooms, 2 1/2 baths, 2-car side entry garage
- Walk-out basement, crawl space or slab foundation, please specify when ordering

Sunroom Warmed By Fireplace

Special features

- 2,414 total square feet of living area
- 9' ceilings throughout this home
- Versatile screened porch connects to master suite, outdoor porch and breakfast room for convenience
- Quiet parlor in the front of the home makes an ideal place for reading a cozy home office
- Future playroom on the second floor has an additional 305 square feet of living area
- 3 bedrooms, 2 1/2 baths, 2-car side entry garage
- Slab foundation

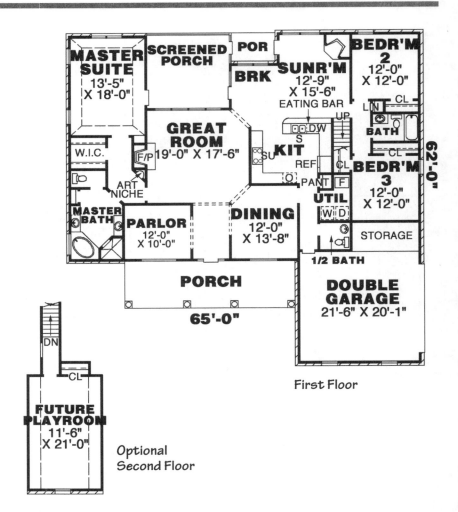

First Floor

Optional Second Floor

Appealing Two-Story For Family Living

Special features

- 2,316 total square feet of living area
- Raised hearth and built-in media center create an impressive feel to the family room
- Expansive kitchen has center island with cooktop range and is open to dining area featuring a trio of skylights
- 9' ceilings throughout first floor
- 3 bedrooms, 2 1/2 baths, 3-car garage
- Walk-out basement or basement foundation, please specify when ordering
- 1,287 square feet on the first floor and 1,029 square feet on the second floor

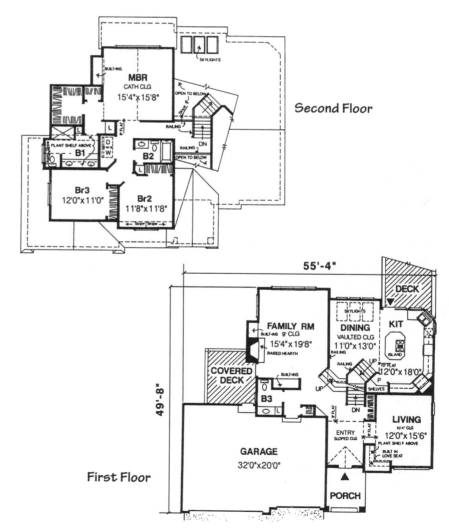

Second Floor

First Floor

Country Flair

Special features

- 1,675 total square feet of living area
- Country flair gives this home curb appeal
- Spacious laundry located off master bedroom
- Cathedral ceiling in living area
- Alternate floor plan design includes handicap accessibility that is 100% ADA compliant
- 3 bedrooms, 2 baths, 2-car side entry garage
- Crawl space or slab foundation, please specify when ordering

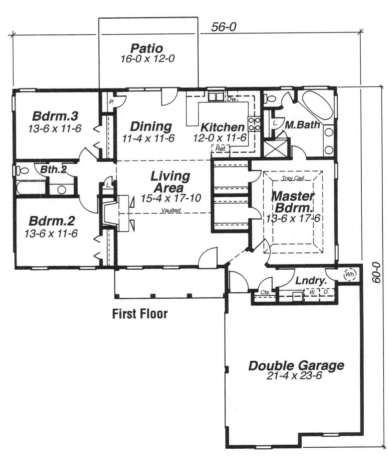

First Floor

Patio
16-0 x 12-0

Bdrm.3
13-6 x 11-6

Dining
11-4 x 11-6

Kitchen
12-0 x 11-6

M.Bath

Bth.2

Living Area
15-4 x 17-10
Vaulted

Master Bdrm.
13-6 x 17-6
Tray Ceil.

Bdrm.2
13-6 x 11-6

Lndry.

Double Garage
21-4 x 23-6

56-0

60-0

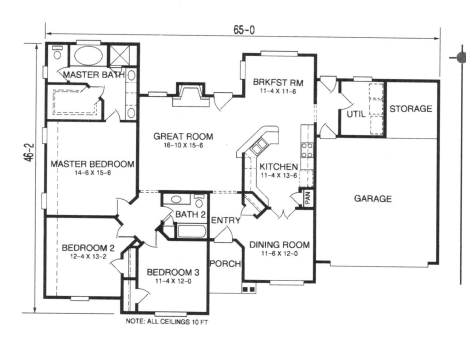

65-0

46-2

MASTER BATH

BRKFST RM
11-4 X 11-6

STORAGE

UTIL

GREAT ROOM
16-10 X 15-6

KITCHEN
11-4 X 13-6

MASTER BEDROOM
14-6 X 15-6

GARAGE

PAN

BATH 2

ENTRY

BEDROOM 2
12-4 X 13-2

DINING ROOM
11-6 X 12-0

PORCH

BEDROOM 3
11-4 X 12-0

NOTE: ALL CEILINGS 10 FT

10' Ceilings

Special features

- 1,862 total square feet of living area
- Comfortable traditional has all the amenities of a larger plan in a compact layout
- Angled eating bar separates kitchen and great room while leaving these areas open to one another for entertaining
- 3 bedrooms, 2 baths, 2-car garage
- Crawl space or slab foundation, please specify when ordering

COPYRIGHT   LARRY E. BELK

Hard To Resist Ranch Home

Special features

- 2,288 total square feet of living area

- Truly sumptuous master suite includes 12' ceiling, his and hers walk-in closets, sitting area and full bath

- Family room features 14' ceiling and a rear window wall with French doors leading to an enormous deck

- Cozy hearth room includes a TV niche

- 3 bedrooms, 2 1/2 baths, 2-car side entry garage

- Basement or crawl space foundation, please specify when ordering

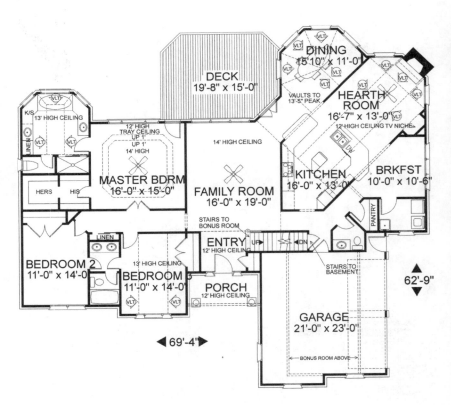

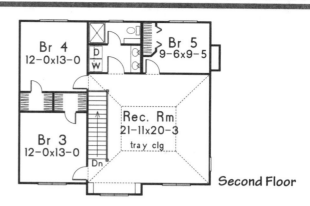

Second Floor

Br 4
12-0x13-0

Br 5
9-6x9-5

Rec. Rm
21-11x20-3
tray clg

Br 3
12-0x13-0

Dn

Great Media Room

Special features

- 2,750 total square feet of living area
- Oversized rooms throughout
- 9' ceilings on first floor
- Unique utility bay workshop off garage
- Spacious master suite with luxurious bath
- Optional sixth bedroom plan also included
- 5 bedrooms, 3 1/2 baths, 2-car side entry garage
- Basement foundation, drawings also include crawl space and slab foundations
- 1,700 square feet on the first floor and 1,050 square feet on the second floor

First Floor

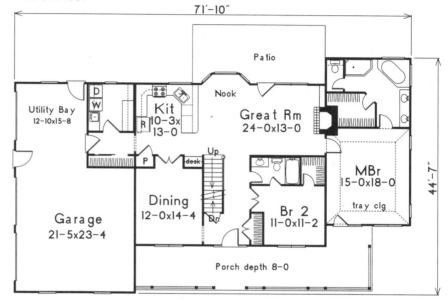

71'-10"

Patio

Nook

Utility Bay
12-10x15-8

Kit
10-3x13-0

Great Rm
24-0x13-0

MBr
15-0x18-0
tray clg

Garage
21-5x23-4

Dining
12-0x14-4

desk

Up

Br 2
11-0x11-2

44'-7"

Porch depth 8-0

A Traditional Feel To This Ranch

Special features

- 1,575 total square feet of living area
- Two secondary bedrooms share a full bath
- Formal dining room features column accents
- Breakfast room has sliding glass doors leading to an outdoor deck
- 3 bedrooms, 2 baths, 2-car garage
- Basement foundation

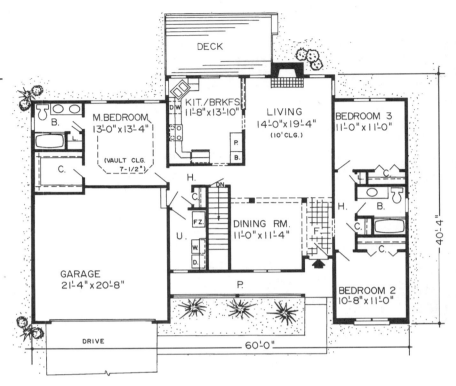

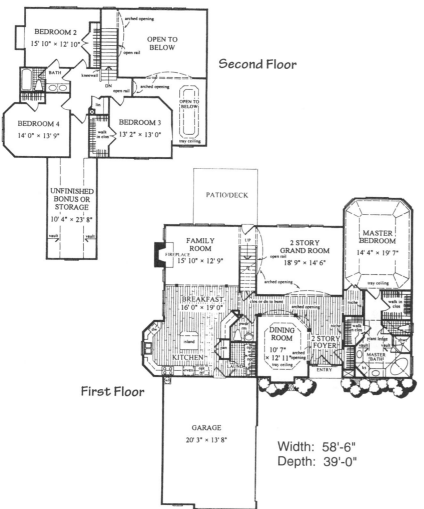

Second Floor

BEDROOM 2
15' 10" × 12' 10"

OPEN TO BELOW

arched opening

open rail

BATH

kneewall

DN

open rail

arched opening

OPEN TO BELOW

lin

BEDROOM 4
14' 0" × 13' 9"

BEDROOM 3
13' 2" × 13' 0"

walk in clos

tray ceiling

UNFINISHED BONUS OR STORAGE
10' 4" × 23' 8"

vault   vault

First Floor

PATIO/DECK

FAMILY ROOM
15' 10" × 12' 9"

FIREPLACE

UP

2 STORY GRAND ROOM
18' 9" × 14' 6"

open rail

MASTER BEDROOM
14' 4" × 19' 7"

tray ceiling

arched opening

BREAKFAST
16' 0" × 19' 0"

clos or dn to bsmt

arched opening

niche

walk in clos

DINING ROOM
10' 7" × 12' 11"

arched opening

2 STORY FOYER

niche

walk in clos

plant ledge

shw

vault

vault

island

KITCHEN

pan

LAUND

tray ceiling

ENTRY

MASTER BATH

oven   opt ref

GARAGE
20' 3" × 13' 8"

Width: 58'-6"
Depth: 39'-0"

Cottage Tudor Design

Special features

- 2,696 total square feet of living area
- Two-story grand room has an elegant feel with arched opening
- Large kitchen has island and lots of cabinetry
- Cozy family room has fireplace
- Bonus room on second floor has an additional 299 square feet of living area
- 4 bedrooms, 2 1/2 baths, 2-car side entry garage
- Basement foundation
- 1,892 square feet on the first floor and 804 square feet on the second floor

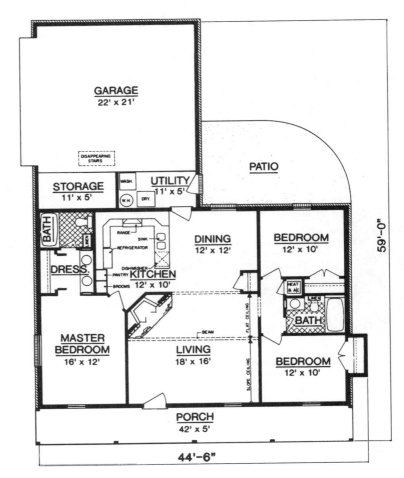

GARAGE
22' x 21'

DISAPPEARING STAIRS

PATIO

STORAGE
11' x 5'

WASH.

W.H.

DRY.

UTILITY
11' x 5'

BATH

RANGE

SINK

REFRIGERATOR

DINING
12' x 12'

BEDROOM
12' x 10'

DRESS.

DISHWASHER

PANTRY

KITCHEN
12' x 10'

BROOMS

HEAT & AC

LINEN

BATH

MASTER BEDROOM
16' x 12'

BEAM

FLAT CEILING

LIVING
18' x 16'

SLOPE CEILING

BEDROOM
12' x 10'

PORCH
42' x 5'

44'-6"

59'-0"

Quaint And Cozy

Special features

- 1,191 total square feet of living area
- Energy efficient home with 2" x 6" exterior walls
- Master bedroom located near living areas for maximum convenience
- Living room has cathedral ceiling and stone fireplace
- 3 bedrooms, 2 baths, 2-car side entry garage
- Slab or crawl space foundation, please specify when ordering

Second Floor

- Attic
- Family Room Below
- Bath
- Bedroom 4 12⁸ x 12⁰ → $12^8 \times 12^0$
- W.i.c.
- LINEN
- OPEN RAIL
- STAIRS DN.
- OVERLOOK
- OPEN RAIL
- W.i.c.
- Foyer Below
- Bedroom 3 $11^0 \times 10^8$
- W.i.c.
- VAULT
- Opt. Bonus Room $11^5 \times 19^2$

Second Floor Overlook

Special features

- 2,126 total square feet of living area
- Second floor includes an optional bonus room with an additional 251 square feet of living area
- Kitchen overlooks vaulted family room with a handy serving bar
- Two-story foyer creates an airy feeling
- 4 bedrooms, 3 baths, 2-car side entry garage
- Walk-out basement, crawl space or slab foundation, please specify when ordering
- 1,583 square feet on the first floor and 543 square feet on the second floor

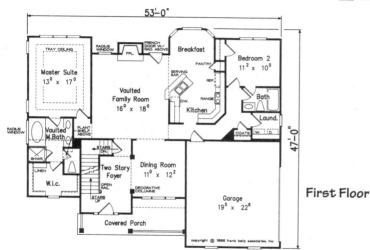

53'-0"

47'-0"

- TRAY CEILING
- RADIUS WINDOW
- FPL
- FRENCH DOOR W/ RAD. ABOVE
- Breakfast
- PANTRY
- Bedroom 2 $11^2 \times 10^0$
- Master Suite $13^0 \times 17^0$
- SERVING BAR
- REF.
- Vaulted Family Room $16^0 \times 18^0$
- DW.
- RANGE
- Kitchen
- Bath
- Laund.
- RADIUS WINDOW
- Vaulted M.Bath
- PLANT SHELF ABOVE
- COATS
- W. D.
- SHWR.
- LINEN
- W.i.c.
- STAIRS DN.
- Two Story Foyer
- OPEN RAIL
- STAIRS UP
- Dining Room $11^0 \times 12^2$
- DECORATIVE COLUMNS
- Garage $19^5 \times 22^8$
- Covered Porch

First Floor

copyright © 1996 frank betz associates, inc.

Quaint Exterior, Full Front Porch

Special features

- 1,657 total square feet of living area
- Stylish pass-through between living and dining areas
- Master bedroom is secluded from living area for privacy
- Large windows in breakfast and dining areas
- 3 bedrooms, 2 1/2 baths, 2-car drive under garage
- Basement foundation
- 1,046 square feet on the first floor and 611 square feet on the second floor

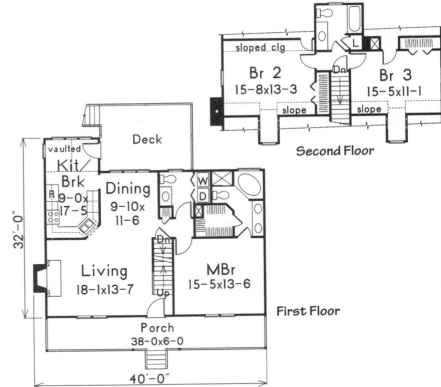

Second Floor

Br 2 15-8x13-3

Br 3 15-5x11-1

sloped clg

slope   slope

First Floor

Deck

vaulted

Kit/ Brk 9-0x 17-5

Dining 9-10x 11-6

Living 18-1x13-7

MBr 15-5x13-6

Porch 38-0x6-0

32'-0"

40'-0"

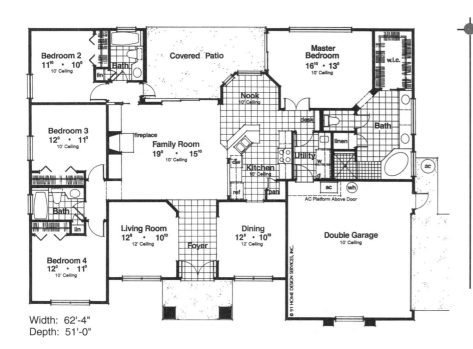

Bedroom 2
11¹⁰ • 10⁰
10' Ceiling

Bath

Covered Patio

Master
Bedroom
16¹⁰ • 13⁰
10' Ceiling

w.l.c.

Nook
10' Ceiling

desk

Bath

Bedroom 3
12⁰ • 11⁰
10' Ceiling

fireplace

Family Room
19⁰ • 15¹⁰
10' Ceiling

linen

Utility

dw

Kitchen
10' Ceiling

Bath

ref

pan

ac

wh

AC Platform Above Door

Living Room
12⁸ • 10¹⁰
12' Ceiling

Foyer

Dining
12⁸ • 10¹⁰
12' Ceiling

Double Garage
10' Ceiling

Bedroom 4
12⁰ • 11⁰
10' Ceiling

'91 HOME DESIGN SERVICES, INC.

Width: 62'-4"
Depth: 51'-0"

Kitchen Designed For Efficiently

Special features

- 2,140 total square feet of living area
- Living and dining areas traditionally separated by foyer
- Media wall and fireplace are located in cozy family room
- Generous master suite has sliding glass doors onto patio, walk-in closet and a private bath
- 4 bedrooms, 3 baths, 2-car side entry garage
- Slab foundation

Second Floor

First Floor

Second Floor Terrace

Special features

- 2,300 total square feet of living area
- Cozy fireplace in master suite
- 9' ceiling on first floor
- Energy efficient home with 2" x 6" exterior walls
- 3 bedrooms, 2 1/2 baths, 2-car side entry garage
- Basement foundation
- 1,067 square feet on the first floor and 1,233 square feet on the second floor

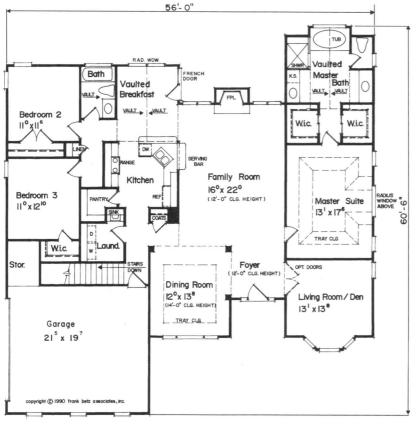

Elaborate Master Suite

Special features

- 2,115 total square feet of living area
- Cozy den/living room has a double-door entry and makes an ideal office space
- Kitchen has serving bar which overlooks vaulted breakfast and family room
- Master suite has all the amenities
- 3 bedrooms, 2 baths, 2-car side entry garage
- Walk-out basement, crawl space or slab foundation, please specify when ordering

Charming Ranch With Angled Floor Plan

Special features

- 1,897 total square feet of living area
- Private office with outdoor entrance could easily serve as a fourth bedroom
- Split bedroom plan includes private master suite with large bath and two walk-in closets
- Beautiful eat-in kitchen with large center island and bayed eating area
- 3 bedrooms, 2 baths, 2-car side entry garage
- Basement, crawl space or slab foundation, please specify when ordering foundation

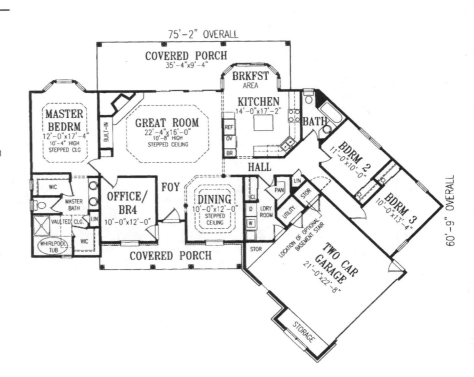

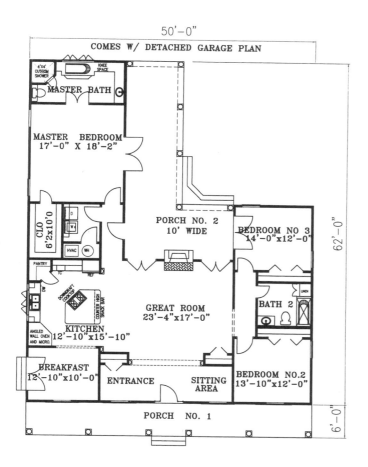

50'-0"

COMES W/ DETACHED GARAGE PLAN

4'x4' CUSTOM SHOWER · KNEE SPACE

MASTER BATH

MASTER BEDROOM
17'-0" X 18'-2"

CLO 6'2x10'0

PANTRY

HVAC · WH

ANGLED WALL OVEN AND MICRO.

DOWNDRAFT COOKTOP

COUNTER HIGH SNACK BAR

KITCHEN
12'-10"x15'-10"

BREAKFAST
12'-10"x10'-0"

ENTRANCE

SITTING AREA

PORCH NO. 2
10' WIDE

GREAT ROOM
23'-4"x17'-0"

BEDROOM NO 3
14'-0"x12'-0"

BATH 2 · LINEN

BEDROOM NO.2
13'-10"x12'-0"

PORCH NO. 1

62'-0"

6'-0"

A Touch Of Home

Special features

- 2,052 total square feet of living area
- Kitchen has large island with cooktop ans snack bar
- Bedroom #3 has access to the rear porch through French doors
- Master bath has large casement windows above whirlpool tub and a 4' x 4' custom shower
- 3 bedrooms, 2 baths, 2-car detached garage
- Crawl space or slab foundation, please specify when ordering

Surrounding Porch For Country Views

Special features

- 1,428 total square feet of living area

- Large vaulted family room opens to dining area and kitchen with breakfast bar and access to surrounding porch

- First floor master suite offers large bath, walk-in closet and nearby laundry facilities

- A spacious loft/bedroom #3 overlooking family room and an additional bedroom and bath conclude the second floor

- 3 bedrooms, 2 baths

- Basement foundation

- 1,013 square feet on the first floor and 415 square feet on the second floor

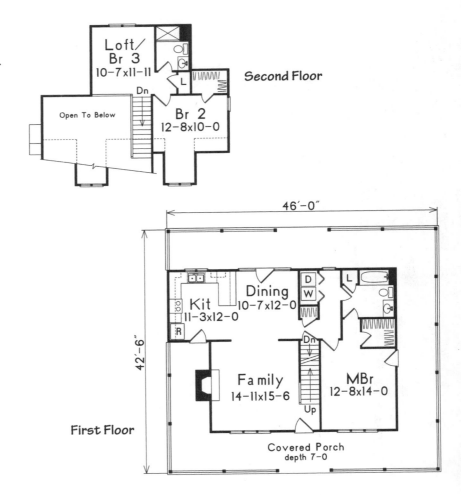

Loft/ Br 3 10-7x11-11

Open To Below

Dn

Br 2 12-8x10-0

Second Floor

46'-0"

42'-6"

Kit 11-3x12-0

Dining 10-7x12-0

D W

L

R

Dn

Family 14-11x15-6

Up

MBr 12-8x14-0

First Floor

Covered Porch depth 7-0

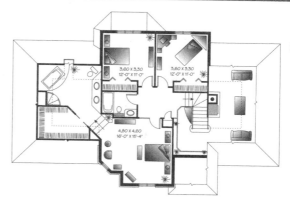

Second Floor

First Floor

Majestic European Traditional

Special features

- 2,310 total square feet of living area
- Snack bar in kitchen for eat-in dining
- Cathedral ceiling in living room
- Energy efficient home with 2" x 6" exterior walls
- 3 bedrooms, 2 1/2 baths, 2-car garage
- Basement foundation
- 1,236 square feet on the first floor and 1,074 square feet on the second floor

A Great Manor House, Spacious Inside And Out

Special features

- 3,368 total square feet of living area
- Sunken great room with cathedral ceiling, wooden beams, skylights and a masonry fireplace
- Octagon-shaped breakfast room has domed ceiling with beams, large windows and door to patio
- Master bedroom in a private wing with deluxe bath and dressing area
- Oversized walk-in closets and storage areas in each bedroom
- 4 bedrooms, 3 full baths, 2 half baths, 2-car side entry garage
- Basement foundation
- 2,150 square feet on the first floor and 1,218 square feet on the second floor

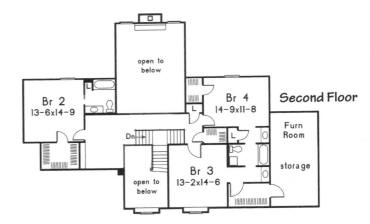

Second Floor

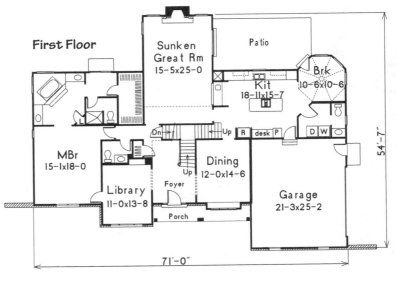

First Floor

Outdoor Living Indoors With Covered Patio

Special features

- 2,793 total square feet of living area
- Beautiful curved staircase invites guests into home
- Large great room stretches from the front to the back of the first floor
- Master suite has many amenities
- Future play room has an additional 285 square feet of living area
- 4 bedrooms, 3 1/2 baths, 3-car rear entry garage
- Crawl space or slab foundation, please specify when ordering
- 1,900 square feet on the first floor and 893 square feet on the second floor

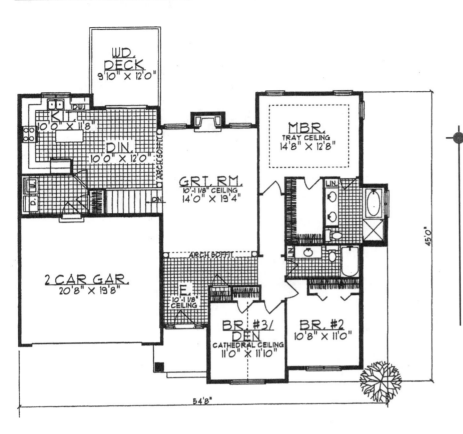

WD. DECK
9'10" X 12'0"

K.
10'0" X 11'8"

DIN.
10'0" X 12'0"

MBR.
TRAY CEILING
14'8" X 12'8"

GRT. RM.
10'-1 1/8" CEILING
14'0" X 19'4"

LIN

ARCH SOFFIT

2 CAR GAR.
20'8" X 19'8"

ARCH SOFFIT

E.
10'-1 1/8" CEILING

LIN

BR. #3/ DEN
CATHEDRAL CEILING
11'0" X 11'10"

BR. #2
10'8" X 11'0"

45'0"

54'8"

Narrow Lot Charmer
Special features
- 1,600 total square feet of living area
- Optional den with cathedral ceiling
- Kitchen has a large island for additional counterspace
- Master bedroom has a large walk-in closet and a full bath with double vanity
- 3 bedrooms, 2 baths, 2-car garage
- Basement foundation

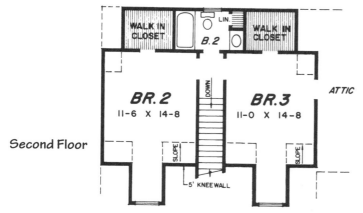

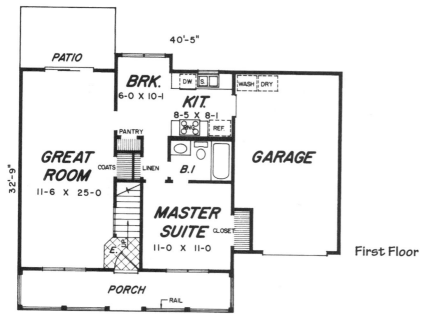

Second Floor

WALK IN CLOSET

B.2

LIN.

WALK IN CLOSET

BR.2
11-6 X 14-8

DOWN

BR.3
11-0 X 14-8

ATTIC

SLOPE

SLOPE

5' KNEE WALL

First Floor

40'-5"

PATIO

BRK.
6-0 X 10-1

DW S.

WASH DRY

KIT.
8-5 X 8-1

RNG REF.

PANTRY

32'-9"

GREAT ROOM
11-6 X 25-0

COATS LINEN

B.1

GARAGE

MASTER SUITE
11-0 X 11-0

CLOSET

UP

PORCH

RAIL

Lovely Front Dormers

Special features

- 1,270 total square feet of living area
- Convenient master suite on first floor
- Two secondary bedrooms on second floor each have a large walk-in closet and share a full bath
- Sunny breakfast room has lots of sunlight and easy access to great room and kitchen
- 3 bedrooms, 2 baths, 1-car garage
- Slab or crawl space foundation, please specify when ordering
- 722 square feet on the first floor and 548 square feet on the second floor

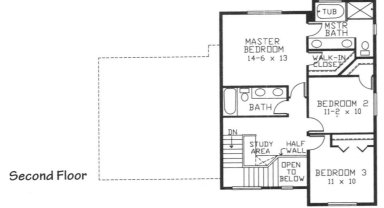

Second Floor

MASTER BEDROOM
14-6 x 13

TUB

MSTR BATH

WALK-IN CLOSET

BATH

BEDROOM 2
11-2 x 10

DN

STUDY AREA

HALF WALL

OPEN TO BELOW

BEDROOM 3
11 x 10

Second Floor Study Area

Special features

- 1,751 total square feet of living area
- Charming covered front porch
- Elegant two-story entry
- Beautifully designed great room with fireplace opens to kitchen
- Large eating counter and walk-in pantry
- Second floor study area perfect for a growing family
- 3 bedrooms, 2 1/2 baths, 2-car garage
- Crawl space foundation
- 922 square feet on the first floor and 829 square feet on the second floor

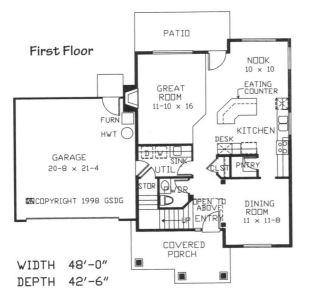

First Floor

PATIO

NOOK
10 x 10

GREAT ROOM
11-10 x 16

EATING COUNTER

FURN

HWT

KITCHEN

DESK

GARAGE
20-8 x 21-4

D W
SINK

UTIL

CLST

PANTRY

STOR

PWDR

COPYRIGHT 1998 GSDG

OPEN TO ABOVE!

ENTRY

UP

DINING ROOM
11 x 11-8

COVERED PORCH

WIDTH   48'-0"
DEPTH   42'-6"

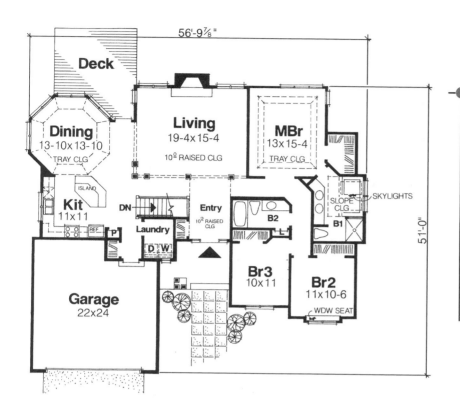

Deck

Dining
13-10 x 13-10
TRAY CLG

ISLAND

Kit
11x11

DN

Living
19-4 x 15-4
10² RAISED CLG

MBr
13 x 15-4
TRAY CLG

SLOPE CLG

SKYLIGHTS

Entry
10² RAISED CLG

B2

B1

REF
P
DW
Laundry

Br3
10 x 11

Br2
11 x 10-6

WDW SEAT

Garage
22x24

56'-9⅞"

51'-0"

Octagon-Shaped Dining Area

Special features

- 1,753 total square feet of living area
- Sloped ceiling and skylights brighten master bath
- Living room flooded with sunlight from windows flanking fireplace
- Kitchen has large island ideal for workspace or dining
- 3 bedrooms, 2 baths, 2-car garage
- Basement foundation

© Urban Design Group, Inc.   A|B|D

Luxurious Ranch Filled With Fantastic Features

Special features

- 2,088 total square feet of living area
- Exceptional master suite includes grand bath, spacious walk-in closet, direct access to deck and a unique secluded morning porch
- An abundance of windows brighten the breakfast room and kitchen
- Vaulted and raised ceilings adorn the foyer, kitchen, master suite, living, family and dining rooms
- 3 bedrooms, 2 1/2 baths, 2-car garage
- Basement, crawl space or slab foundation, please specify when ordering

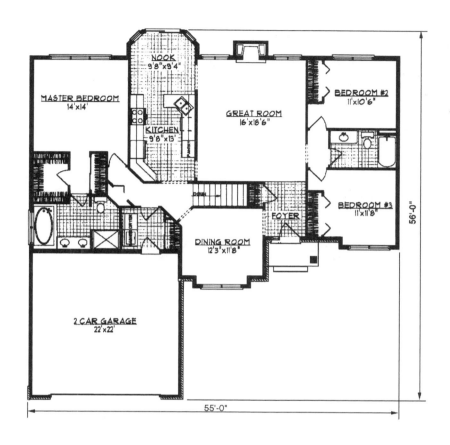

NOOK
9'8"x9'4"

MASTER BEDROOM
14'x14'

GREAT ROOM
16'x18'6"

BEDROOM #2
11'x10'6"

KITCHEN
9'8"x13'

BEDROOM #3
11'x11'8"

FOYER

DINING ROOM
12'3'x11'8"

2 CAR GARAGE
22'x22'

56'-0"

55'-0"

Great Dining Room For Entertaining

Special features

- 1,730 total square feet of living area
- Energy efficient home with 2" x 6" exterior walls
- All bedrooms are large and open with plenty of closet space
- Great room is cheerful and bright and includes a cozy fireplace
- 3 bedrooms, 2 baths, 2-car garage
- Basement foundation

Victorian Styled Gazebo Enhances Front Porch

Special features

- 2,084 total square feet of living area
- Charming bay window in master suite allows sunlight in as well as style
- Great room accesses front covered porch extending the living area to the outdoors
- Large playroom on second floor is ideal for family living
- 3 bedrooms, 2 1/2 baths, 2-car side entry garage
- Slab, crawl space or basement foundation, please specify when ordering
- 1,203 square feet on the first floor and 881 square feet on the second floor

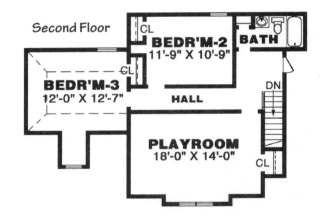

Second Floor

BEDR'M-2
11'-9" X 10'-9"

BATH

CL

CL

BEDR'M-3
12'-0" X 12'-7"

HALL

DN

PLAYROOM
18'-0" X 14'-0"

CL

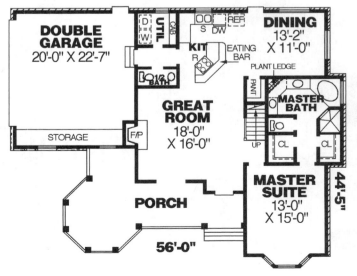

First Floor

DOUBLE GARAGE
20'-0" X 22'-7"

UTIL

KIT

RER

DINING
13'-2" X 11'-0"

PLANT LEDGE

BATH

GREAT ROOM
18'-0" X 16'-0"

MASTER BATH

PANT

STORAGE

F/P

UP

CL

CL

PORCH

MASTER SUITE
13'-0" X 15'-0"

44'-5"

56'-0"

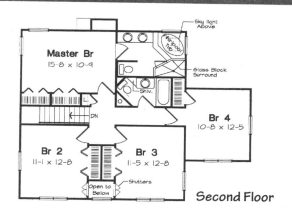

Second Floor

Master Br
15-8 x 10-9

Sky light Above

Glass Block Surround

Shlv.

DN

Br 4
10-8 x 12-5

Br 2
11-1 x 12-8

Br 3
11-5 x 12-8

Open to Below

Shutters

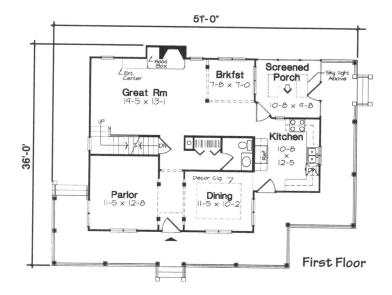

51'-0"

36'-0"

Wood Box

Ent. Center

Brkfst
7-8 x 7-0

Screened Porch
10-8 x 9-8

Sky light Above

Great Rm
19-5 x 13-1

UP

DN

Kitchen
10-8 x 12-5

Ref.

Parlor
11-5 x 12-8

Decor Clg

Dining
11-5 x 10-2

First Floor

Two-Story With Victorian Feel

Special features

- 1,982 total square feet of living area
- Spacious master bedroom has bath with corner whirlpool tub and sunny skylight above
- Breakfast area overlooks into great room
- Screened porch with skylight above extends the home outdoors and allows for entertainment area
- 4 bedrooms, 2 1/2 baths
- Basement foundation
- 999 square feet on the first floor and 983 square feet on the second floor

50-0 WIDE X 42-0 DEPTH
(INCLUDING COVERED PORCH)

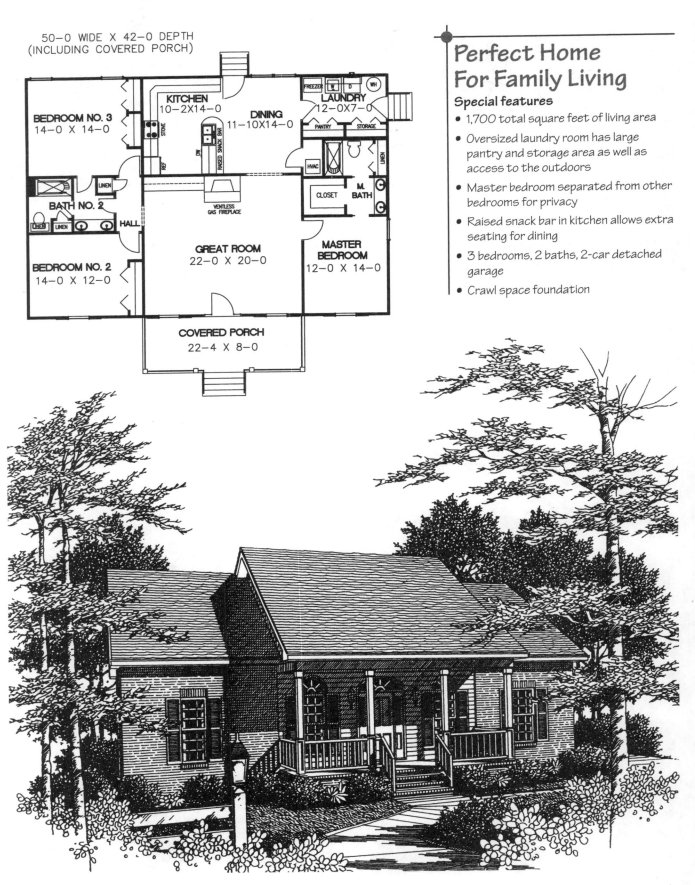

KITCHEN
10-2X14-0

DINING
11-10X14-0

LAUNDRY
12-0X7-0

FREEZER · W · D · WH

PANTRY · STORAGE

BEDROOM NO. 3
14-0 X 14-0

STOVE · DW · REF · RAISED SNACK BAR

LINEN

HVAC

LINEN

BATH NO. 2

LINEN · LINEN · HALL

M. BATH

CLOSET

VENTLESS GAS FIREPLACE

BEDROOM NO. 2
14-0 X 12-0

GREAT ROOM
22-0 X 20-0

MASTER BEDROOM
12-0 X 14-0

COVERED PORCH
22-4 X 8-0

Perfect Home For Family Living

Special features

- 1,700 total square feet of living area
- Oversized laundry room has large pantry and storage area as well as access to the outdoors
- Master bedroom separated from other bedrooms for privacy
- Raised snack bar in kitchen allows extra seating for dining
- 3 bedrooms, 2 baths, 2-car detached garage
- Crawl space foundation

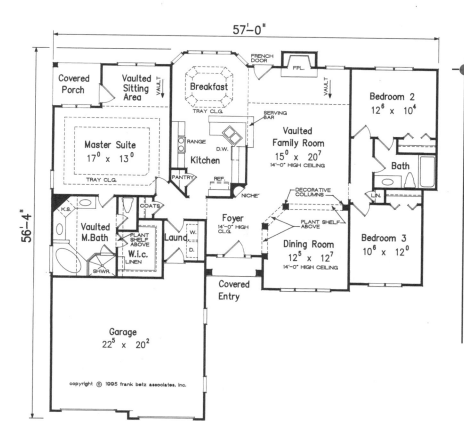

Elaborate Dining Room

Special features

- 1,779 total square feet of living area
- Well-designed floor plan has vaulted family room with fireplace and access to the outdoors
- Decorative columns separate dining area from foyer
- Vaulted ceiling adds spaciousness in master bath with walk-in closet
- 3 bedrooms, 2 baths, 2-car garage
- Walk-out basement, slab or crawl space foundation, please specify when ordering

Stately Front Entrance With Style

Special features

- 2,615 total square feet of living area
- Grand two-story entry features majestic palladian window, double French doors to parlor and access to powder room
- State-of-the-art kitchen has corner sink with two large arch-top windows, island snack bar, menu desk and walk-in pantry
- Master bath is vaulted and offers a luxurious step-up tub, palladian window, built-in shelves and columns with plant shelf
- 4 bedrooms, 2 1/2 baths, 2-car garage
- Basement foundation
- 1,412 square feet on the first floor and 1,203 square feet on the second floor

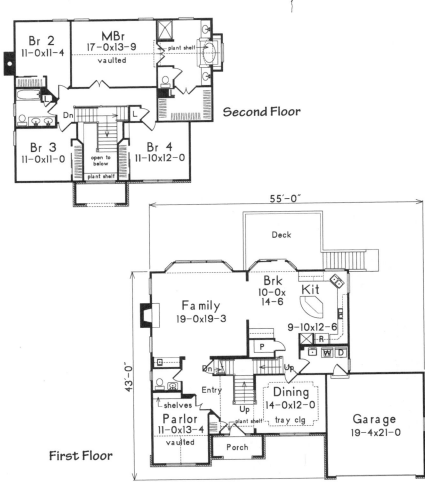

Second Floor

First Floor

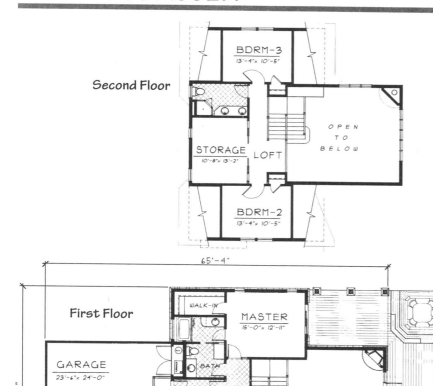

Second Floor

BDRM-3
13'-4" x 10'-5"

STORAGE
10'-8" x 13'-2"

LOFT

OPEN
TO
BELOW

BDRM-2
13'-4" x 10'-5"

65'-4"

First Floor

43'-2"

GARAGE
23'-6" x 24'-0"

WALK-IN

MASTER
15'-0" x 12'-11"

BATH

UTILITY
MUD. ROOM

LIVING RM
18'-2" x 19'-0"

DECK
160 SQ. FT.

DINING
12'-5" x 13'-0"

KITCHEN
12'-7" x 10'-0"

PORCH
COVERED

Truly Unique Design
Special features

- 2,104 total square feet of living area
- 9' ceilings on the first floor
- Living room opens onto deck through double French doors
- Second floor includes large storage room
- 3 bedrooms, 2 baths, 2-car garage
- Crawl space foundation
- 1,435 square feet on the first floor and 669 square feet on the second floor

Charming Country Cottage

Special features

- *864 total square feet of living area*
- *Large laundry area accesses the outdoors as well as the kitchen*
- *Front covered porch creates an ideal outdoor living area*
- *Snack bar in kitchen creates a quick and easy dining area*
- *2 bedrooms, 1 bath*
- *Crawl space or slab foundation, please specify when ordering*

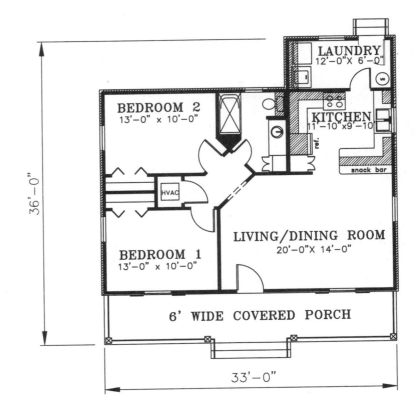

BEDROOM 2
13'-0" x 10'-0"

LAUNDRY
12'-0"X 6'-0"

KITCHEN
11'-10"x9'-10

snack bar

HVAC

BEDROOM 1
13'-0" x 10'-0"

LIVING/DINING ROOM
20'-0"X 14'-0"

36'-0"

6' WIDE COVERED PORCH

33'-0"

Decorative
Plant Ledge
Enhances Interior

Special features

- 2,060 total square feet of living area
- Massive family room with corner fireplace is suitable to large family
- Detailed brickwork and windows give style to exterior
- 4 bedrooms, 2 baths, 2-car garage
- Slab foundation

Width: 50'-0"
Depth: 60'-8"

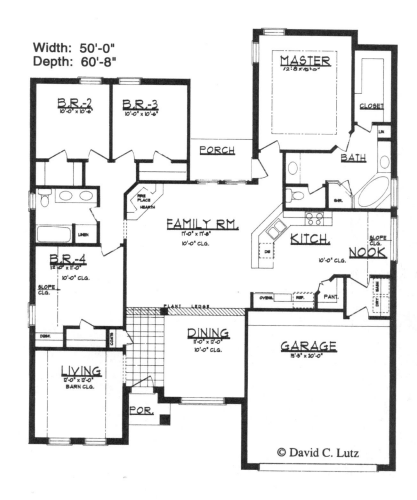

© David C. Lutz

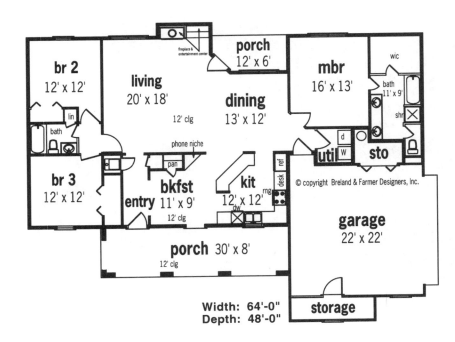

Open Living

Special features

- 1,770 total square feet of living area
- Open floor plan makes this home feel spacious
- 12' ceilings in kitchen, living, breakfast and dining areas
- Kitchen is the center of activity with views into all gathering places
- 3 bedrooms, 2 baths, 2-car side entry garage
- Slab or crawl space foundation, please specify when ordering

Width: 64'-0"
Depth: 48'-0"

Traditional Brick Ranch

Special features

- 2,697 total square feet of living area
- Secluded study with full bath nearby is an ideal guest room or office
- Master bedroom has access to outdoor patio
- Additional 351 square feet of unfinished attic space
- 3 bedrooms, 3 baths, 2-car side entry garage
- Slab foundation

Width: 59'-10"
Depth: 60'-10"

Ma. Bath

Garage
23'-4" X 20'-7"

Patio

Breakfast
9'-0" X 13'-0"

Util.

Ma. Bedroom
14'-3" X 17'-0"

Living
20'-1" X 18'-0"

Kitchen
12'-7" X 12'-6"

Bath 2

Bath 3

Bedroom 2
10'-9" X 13'-0"

Foyer

Dining
11'-4" X 13'-0"

Study
10'-8" X 12'-0"

Bedroom 3
11'-6" X 11'-0"

Porch

Floor-To-Ceiling Window Expands Compact Two-Story

Special features

- 1,246 total square feet of living area
- Corner living room window adds openness and light
- Out-of-the-way kitchen with dining area accesses the outdoors
- Private first floor master bedroom with corner window
- Large walk-in closet is located in bedroom #3
- Easily built perimeter allows economical construction
- 3 bedrooms, 2 baths, 2-car garage
- Basement foundation
- 846 square feet on the first floor and 400 square feet on the second floor

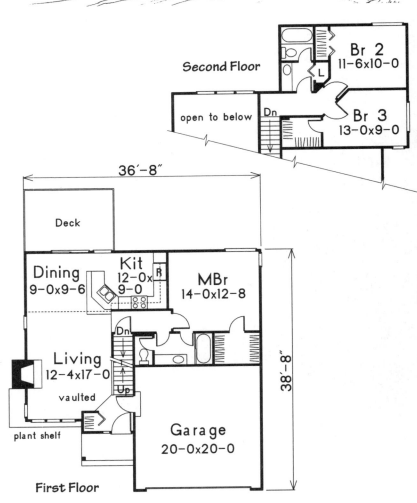

Second Floor

Br 2 11-6x10-0

open to below   Dn

Br 3 13-0x9-0

36'-8"

Deck

Dining 9-0x9-6

Kit 12-0x 9-0

MBr 14-0x12-8

38'-8"

Living 12-4x17-0

vaulted

plant shelf

Garage 20-0x20-0

First Floor

Covered Breezeway To Garage

Special features

- 1,406 total square feet of living area
- Master bedroom has sloped ceiling
- Kitchen and dining area merge becoming a gathering place
- Enter family room from charming covered front porch and find fireplace and lots of windows
- 3 bedrooms, 2 baths, 2-car detached garage
- Slab or crawl space foundation, please specify when ordering

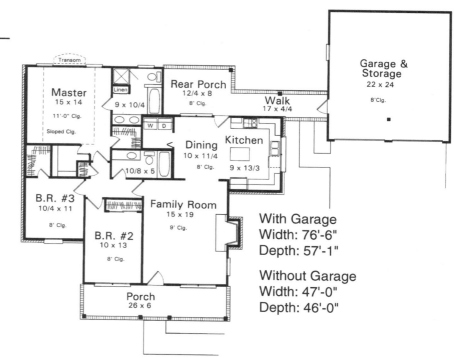

With Garage
Width: 76'-6"
Depth: 57'-1"

Without Garage
Width: 47'-0"
Depth: 46'-0"

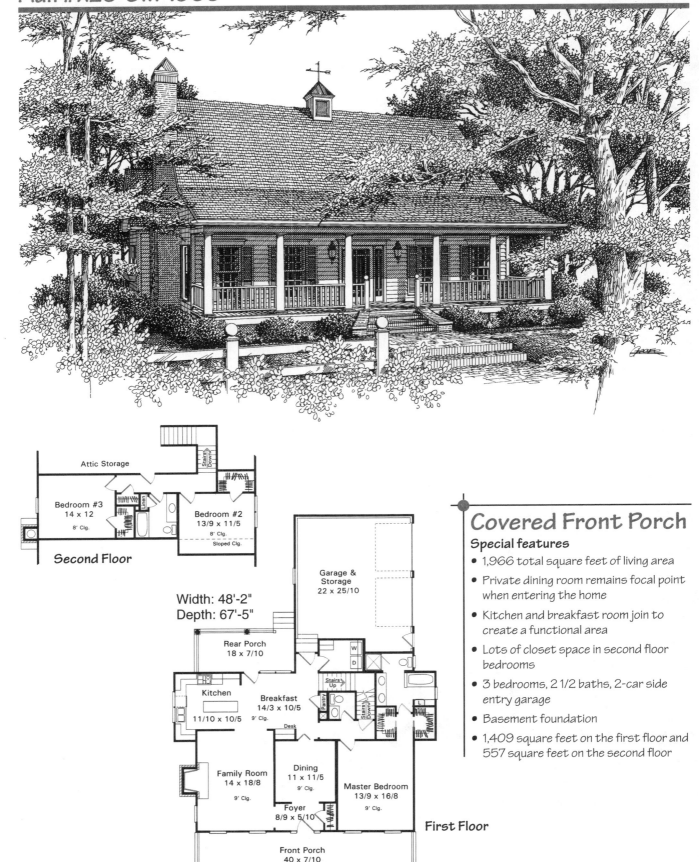

Width: 48'-2"
Depth: 67'-5"

Attic Storage

Bedroom #3
14 x 12
8' Clg.

Linen

Bedroom #2
13/9 x 11/5
8' Clg.
Sloped Clg.

Second Floor

Stairs Down

Garage & Storage
22 x 25/10

Rear Porch
18 x 7/10

W
D

Stairs Up

Kitchen
11/10 x 10/5

Breakfast
14/3 x 10/5
9' Clg.

Pantry

Stairs Down

Desk

Family Room
14 x 18/8
9' Clg.

Dining
11 x 11/5
9' Clg.

Master Bedroom
13/9 x 16/8
9' Clg.

Foyer
8/9 x 5/10

First Floor

Front Porch
40 x 7/10

Covered Front Porch
Special features
- 1,966 total square feet of living area
- Private dining room remains focal point when entering the home
- Kitchen and breakfast room join to create a functional area
- Lots of closet space in second floor bedrooms
- 3 bedrooms, 2 1/2 baths, 2-car side entry garage
- Basement foundation
- 1,409 square feet on the first floor and 557 square feet on the second floor

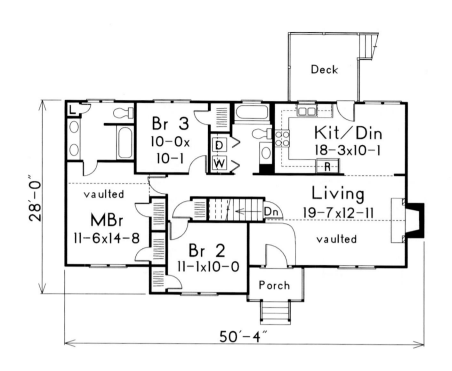

Compact Home For Functional Living

Special features

- 1,220 total square feet of living area
- Vaulted ceilings add luxury to living room and master suite
- Spacious living room accented with a large fireplace and hearth
- Gracious dining area is adjacent to the convenient wrap-around kitchen
- Washer and dryer handy to the bedrooms
- Covered porch entry adds appeal
- Rear sun deck adjoins dining area
- 3 bedrooms, 2 baths, 2-car drive under garage
- Basement foundation

Country-Style With Wrap-Around Porch

Special features

- 1,597 total square feet of living area
- Spacious family room includes fireplace and coat closet
- Open kitchen and dining room provides breakfast bar and access to the outdoors
- Convenient laundry area located near kitchen
- Secluded master suite with walk-in closet and private bath
- 4 bedrooms, 2 1/2 baths, 2-car detached garage
- Basement foundation
- 982 square feet on the first floor and 615 square feet on the second floor

Private Breakfast Room Provides Casual Dining

Special features

- 1,708 total square feet of living area
- Massive family room enhanced with several windows, fireplace and access to porch
- Deluxe master bath accented by step-up corner tub flanked by double vanities
- Closets throughout maintain organized living
- Bedrooms isolated from living areas
- 3 bedrooms, 2 baths, 2-car garage
- Basement foundation, drawings also include crawl space foundation

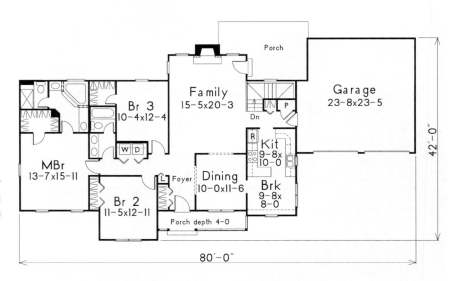

Dramatic Layout Created By Victorian Turret

Special features

- 2,050 total square feet of living area
- Large kitchen/dining area with access to garage and porch
- Master bedroom suite features unique turret design, private bath and large walk-in closet
- Laundry facilities conveniently located near bedrooms
- 3 bedrooms, 2 1/2 baths, 2-car side entry garage
- Basement foundation, drawings also include crawl space and slab foundations
- 1,028 square feet on the first floor and 1,022 square feet on the second floor

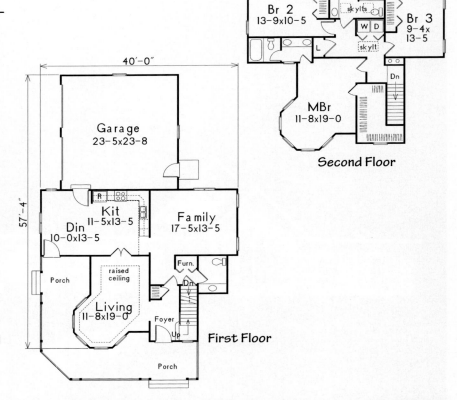

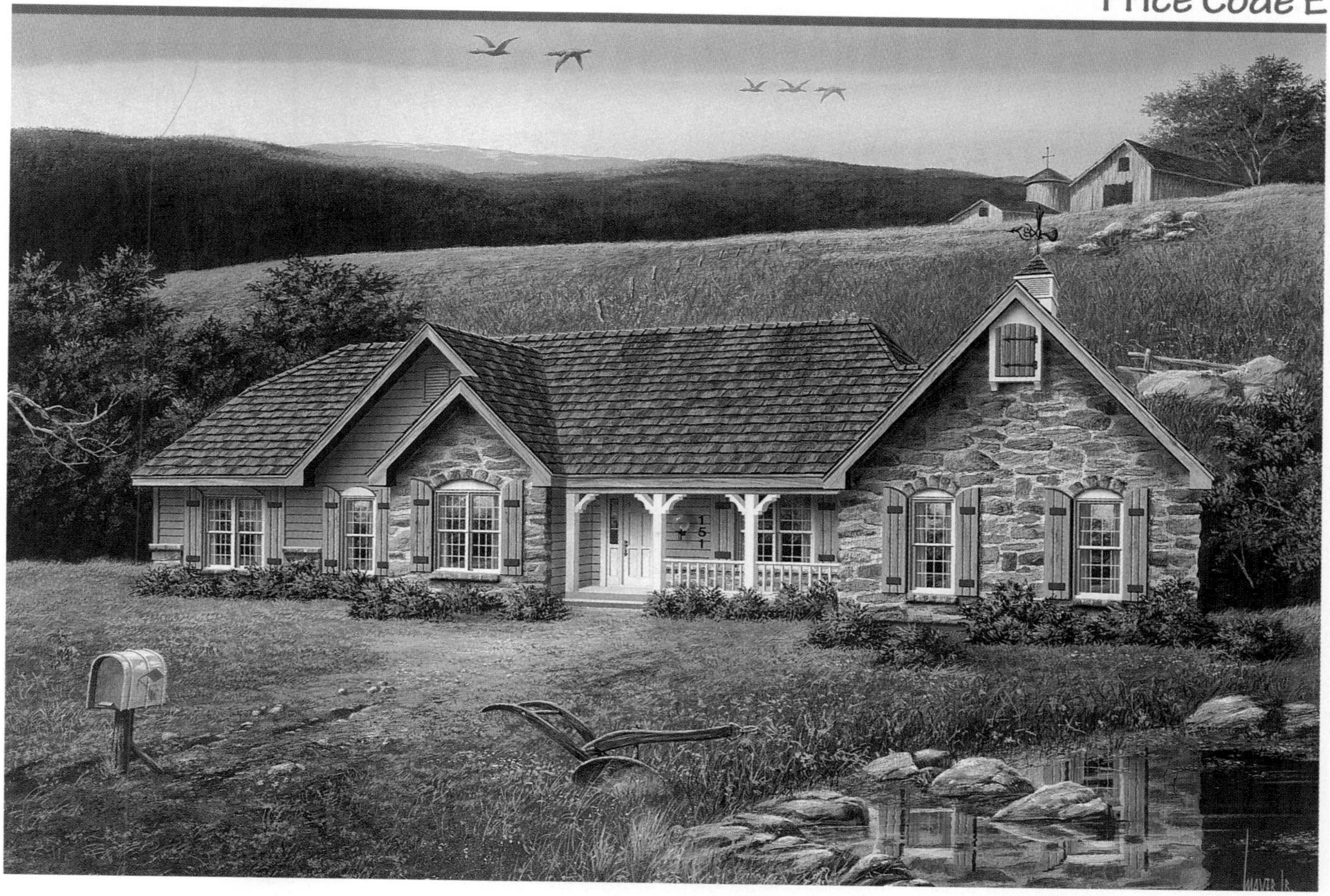

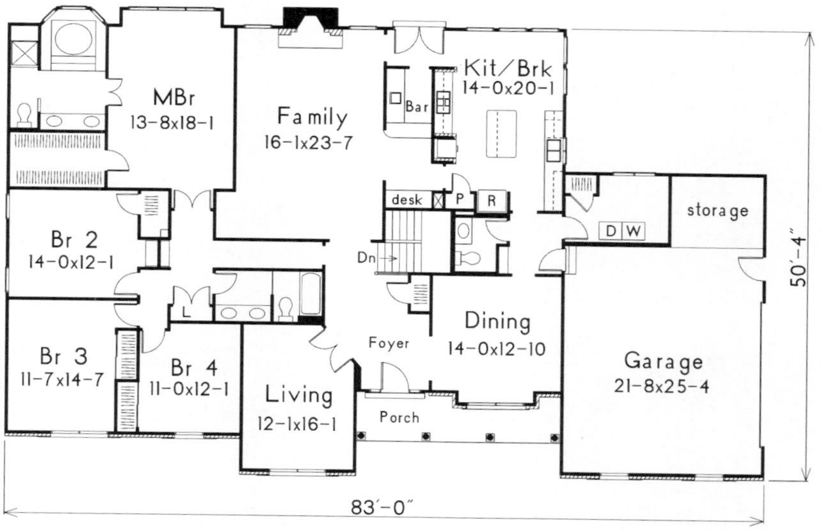

MBr
13-8x18-1
Family
16-1x23-7
Kit/Brk
14-0x20-1
Bar
desk
P
R
Br 2
14-0x12-1
storage
D W
Dn
Br 3
11-7x14-7
L
Br 4
11-0x12-1
Foyer
Dining
14-0x12-10
Garage
21-8x25-4
Living
12-1x16-1
Porch
50'-4"
83'-0"

Massive Ranch With Classy Features

Special features

- 2,874 total square feet of living area
- Large family room with sloped ceiling and wood beams adjoins the kitchen and breakfast area with windows on two walls
- Large foyer opens to family room with massive stone fireplace and open stairs to the basement
- Private master bedroom with raised tub under the bay window, dramatic dressing area and a huge walk-in closet
- 4 bedrooms, 2 1/2 baths, 2-car side entry garage
- Basement foundation

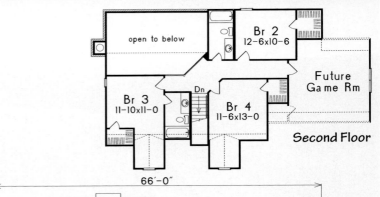

Second Floor

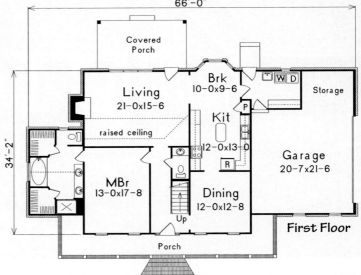

First Floor

Attractive Entry Created By Full-Length Porch

Special features

- 2,357 total square feet of living area
- 9' ceilings on first floor
- Secluded master bedroom includes private bath with double walk-in closets and vanity
- Balcony overlooks living room with large fireplace
- Second floor has three bedrooms and an expansive game room
- 4 bedrooms, 3 1/2 baths, 2-car side entry garage
- Slab foundation, drawings also include crawl space foundation
- 1,492 square feet on the first floor and 865 square feet on the second floor

Classic Atrium Ranch With Rooms To Spare

Special features

- 1,977 total square feet of living area

- Classic traditional exterior always in style

- Spacious great room boasts a vaulted ceiling, dining area, atrium with elegant staircase and feature windows

- Atrium open to 1,416 square feet of optional living area below which consists of an optional family room, two bedrooms, two baths and a study

- 4 bedrooms, 2 1/2 baths, 3-car side entry garage

- Walk-out basement foundation

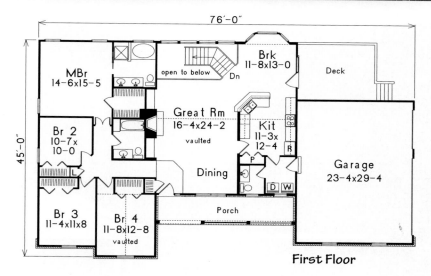

First Floor

Optional Lower Level

Functional Layout For Comfortable Living

Special features

- 1,360 total square feet of living area
- Kitchen/dining room features island work space and plenty of dining area
- Master bedroom with large walk-in closet and private bath
- Laundry room adjacent to the kitchen for easy access
- Convenient workshop in garage
- Large closets in secondary bedrooms
- 3 bedrooms, 2 baths, 2-car side entry garage
- Basement foundation, drawings also include crawl space and slab foundations

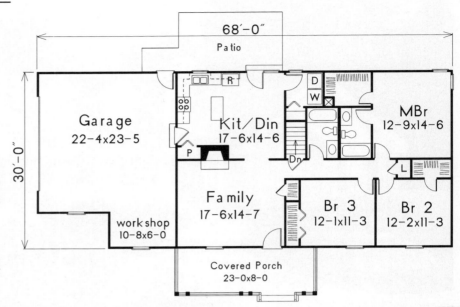

Small Home Is Remarkably Spacious

Special features

- 914 total square feet of living area
- Large porch for leisure evenings
- Dining area with bay window, open stair and pass-through kitchen creates openness
- Basement includes generous garage space, storage area, finished laundry and mechanical room
- 2 bedrooms, 1 bath, 2-car drive under garage
- Basement foundation
- 796 square feet on the first floor and 118 square feet on the lower level

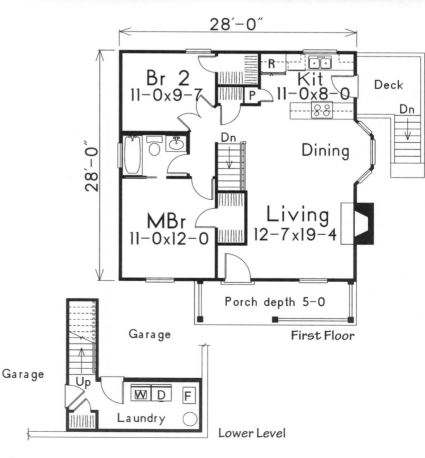

28'-0"

28'-0"

Br 2
11-0x9-7

Kit
11-0x8-0

Deck

Dn

Dn

Dining

MBr
11-0x12-0

Living
12-7x19-4

Porch depth 5-0

First Floor

Garage

Garage

Up

W D F

Laundry

Lower Level

Distinguished Styling For A Small Lot

Special features

- 1,268 total square feet of living area
- Multiple gables, large porch and arched windows create classy exterior
- Innovative design provides openness in great room, kitchen and breakfast room
- Secondary bedrooms have private hall with bath
- 3 bedrooms, 2 baths, 2-car garage
- Basement foundation, drawings also include crawl space and slab foundations

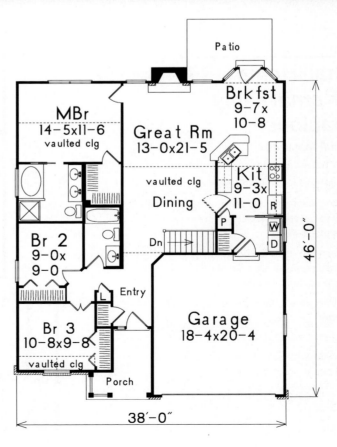

Ultimate Atrium
For A Sloping Lot

Special features

- 3,814 total square feet of living area

- Massive sunken great room with vaulted ceiling includes exciting balcony overlook of towering atrium window wall

- Breakfast bar adjoins open "California" kitchen

- Seven vaulted rooms for drama and four fireplaces for warmth

- Master bath complemented by colonnade and fireplace surrounding sunken tub and deck

- 3 bedrooms, 2 1/2 baths, 3-car side entry garage

- Walk-out basement foundation

- 3,566 square feet on the first floor and 248 square feet on the lower level atrium

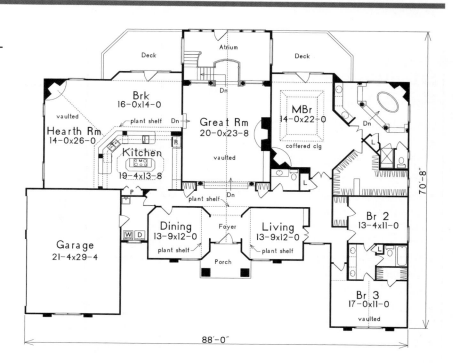

Rear View

Stylish Retreat For A Narrow Lot

Special features

- 1,084 total square feet of living area
- Delightful country porch for quiet evenings
- The living room offers a front feature window which invites the sun and includes a fireplace and dining area with private patio
- The U-shaped kitchen features lots of cabinets and bayed breakfast room with built-in pantry
- Both bedrooms have walk-in closets and access to their own bath
- 2 bedrooms, 2 baths
- Basement foundation

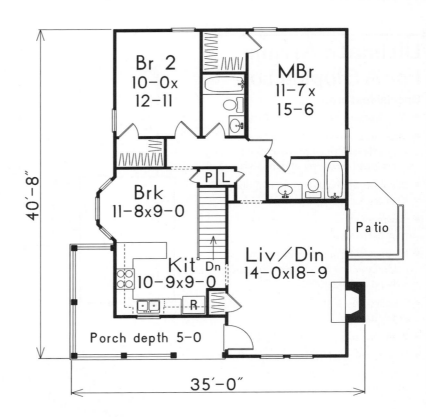

Plan #X26-0739

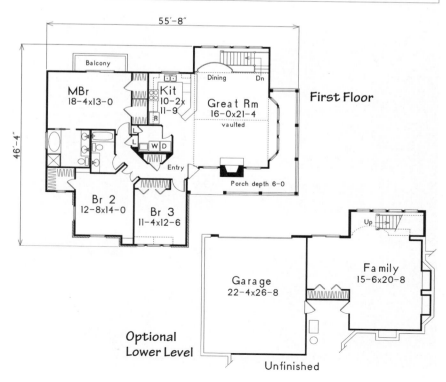

Rear View

A Special Home For Views

Special features

- 1,684 total square feet of living area
- Delightful wrap-around porch anchored by full masonry fireplace
- The vaulted great room includes a large bay window, fireplace, dining balcony and atrium window wall
- His and hers walk-in closets, large luxury bath and sliding doors to exterior balcony are a few fantastic features of the master bedroom
- 3 bedrooms, 2 baths, 2-car drive under garage
- Walk-out basement foundation
- Atrium open to 611 square feet of optional living area on the lower level

55'-8"

46'-4"

Balcony

MBr 18-4x13-0

Kit 10-2x 11-9

Dining Dn

Great Rm 16-0x21-4 vaulted

First Floor

Entry

Porch depth 6-0

Br 2 12-8x14-0

Br 3 11-4x12-6

Up

Garage 22-4x26-8

Family 15-6x20-8

Optional Lower Level

Unfinished

Stately Country Home For The "Spacious Age"

Special features

- 2,727 total square feet of living area
- Wrap-around porch and large foyer create impressive entrance
- A state-of-the-art vaulted kitchen has walk-in pantry and is open to the breakfast room and adjoining screened porch
- A walk-in wet bar, fireplace bay window and deck access are features of the family room
- Vaulted master bedroom suite enjoys a luxurious bath with skylight and an enormous 13' deep walk-in closet
- 4 bedrooms, 2 1/2 baths, 2-car side entry garage
- Walk-out basement foundation
- 1,523 square feet on the first floor and 1,204 square feet on the second floor

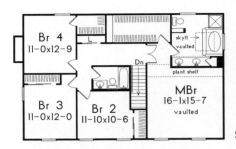

Second Floor

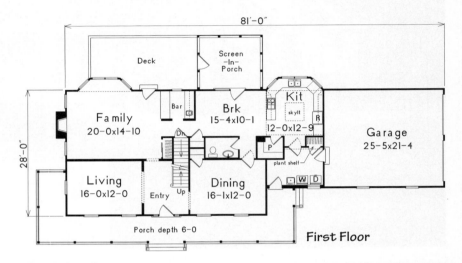

First Floor

Atrium Living For Views On A Narrow Lot

Special features

- 1,231 total square feet of living area

- Dutch gables and stone accents provide an enchanting appearance for a small cottage

- The spacious living room offers a masonry fireplace, atrium with window wall and is open to a dining area with bay window

- A breakfast counter, lots of cabinet space and glass sliding doors to a walk-out balcony create a sensational kitchen

- 380 square feet of optional living area on the lower level

- 2 bedrooms, 2 baths, 1-car drive under garage

- Walk-out basement foundation

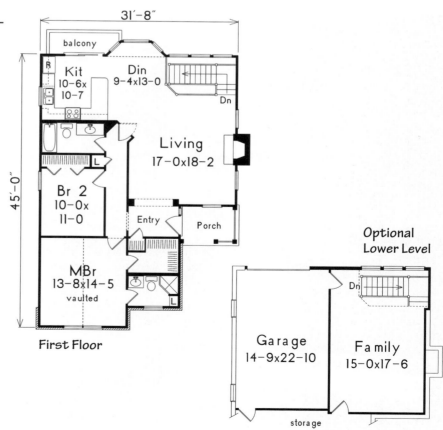

First Floor

Optional Lower Level

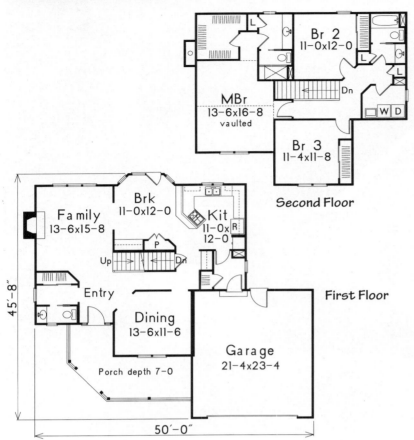

Second Floor

Br 2
11-0x12-0

MBr
13-6x16-8
vaulted

Br 3
11-4x11-8

First Floor

Family
13-6x15-8

Brk
11-0x12-0

Kit
11-0x12-0

Entry

Dining
13-6x11-6

Garage
21-4x23-4

Porch depth 7-0

45'-8"

50'-0"

Angled Porch Greets Guests

Special features

- 2,059 total square feet of living area
- Large desk and pantry add to the breakfast room
- Laundry is located on second floor near bedrooms
- Vaulted ceiling in master suite
- Mud room is conveniently located near garage
- 3 bedrooms, 2 1/2 baths, 2-car garage
- Basement foundation
- 1,043 square feet on the first floor and 1,016 square feet on the second floor

Simple And Cozy

Special features

- 1,392 total square feet of living area
- Centralized great room welcomes guests with a warm fireplace
- Master suite has separate entrance for added privacy
- Kitchen includes breakfast room, snack counter and laundry area
- 3 bedrooms, 2 baths, 2-car garage
- Basement foundation

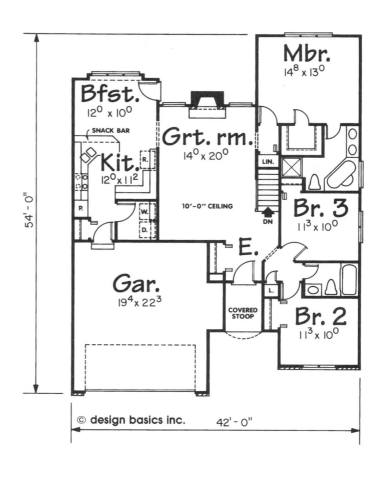

Appealing Gabled Facade

Special features

- 1,680 total square feet of living area
- Vaulted great room has a wet bar making it an ideal space for entertaining
- Spacious dining area features an eating bar for additional seating
- Fourth bedroom could easily be converted to a study
- 4 bedrooms, 2 baths, 2-car garage
- Slab foundation

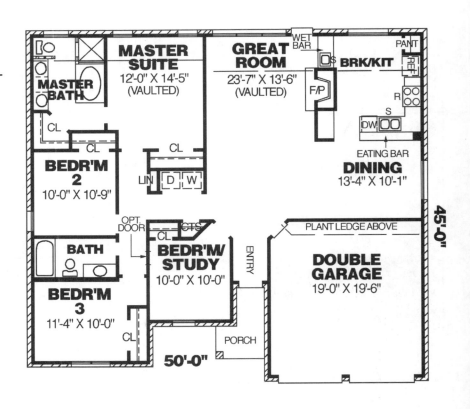

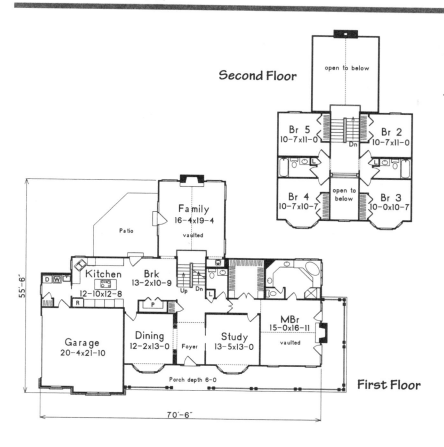

Second Floor

Br 5
10-7x11-0

Br 2
10-7x11-0

open to below

Dn

Br 4
10-7x10-7

open to below

Br 3
10-0x10-7

Family
16-4x19-4
vaulted

Patio

Kitchen
12-10x12-8

D W

R

Brk
13-2x10-9

Up Dn

Garage
20-4x21-10

Dining
12-2x13-0

P

Foyer

Study
13-5x13-0

MBr
15-0x16-11
vaulted

Porch depth 6-0

55'-6"

70'-6"

First Floor

Five Bedroom Home Embraces Large Family

Special features

- 2,828 total square feet of living area
- Popular wrap-around porch gives home country charm
- Secluded, oversized family room with vaulted ceiling and wet bar features many windows
- Any chef would be delighted to cook in this smartly designed kitchen with island and corner windows
- Spectacular master bedroom and bath
- 5 bedrooms, 3 1/2 baths, 2-car side entry garage
- Basement foundation, drawings also include crawl space and slab foundations
- 2,006 square feet on the first floor and 822 square feet on the second floor

Ranch-Style Home With Many Extras

Special features

- 1,295 total square feet of living area
- Wrap-around porch is a lovely place for dining
- A fireplace gives a stunning focal point to the great room that is heightened with a sloped ceiling
- The master suite is full of luxurious touches such as a walk-in closet and a lush private bath
- 2 bedrooms, 2 baths, 2-car garage
- Basement foundation

Width: 62-6"
Depth: 42'-6"

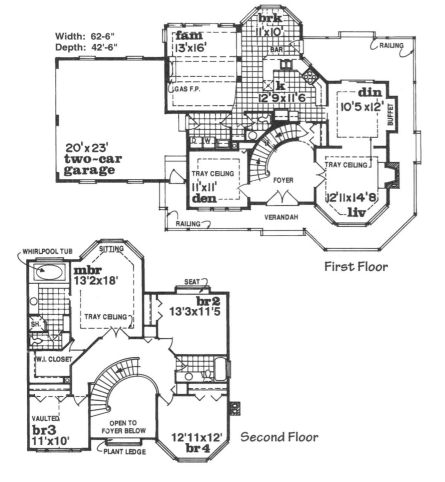

brk
11'x10'

fam
13'x16'

RAILING

BAR

GAS F.P.

k
12'9x11'6

din
10'5 x12'

BUFFET

20' x 23'
**two-car
garage**

TRAY CEILING

D W

TRAY CEILING
11'x11'
den

FOYER

12'11x14'8
liv

RAILING

VERANDAH

First Floor

WHIRLPOOL TUB

SITTING

mbr
13'2x18'

SEAT

br2
13'3x11'5

TRAY CEILING

SH.

W.I. CLOSET

OPEN TO
FOYER BELOW

VAULTED
br3
11'x10'

PLANT LEDGE

12'11x12'
br 4

Second Floor

Appealing
Victorian Accents

Special features

- 2,516 total square feet of living area
- Living room has a fireplace, while the formal dining room has a buffet alcove and access to the verandah
- A cozy sitting area and tray ceiling accent the master bedroom
- Spacious bedrooms make this a wonderful family home
- 4 bedrooms, 2 1/2 baths, 2-car side entry garage
- Basement or crawl space foundation, please specify when ordering
- 1,324 square feet on the first floor and 1,192 square feet on the second floor

Traditional Southern Style Home

Special features

- 1,785 total square feet of living area
- 9' ceilings throughout home
- Luxurious master bath includes whirlpool tub and separate shower
- Cozy breakfast area is convenient to kitchen
- 3 bedrooms, 3 baths, 2-car detached garage
- Basement, crawl or slab foundation, please specify when ordering

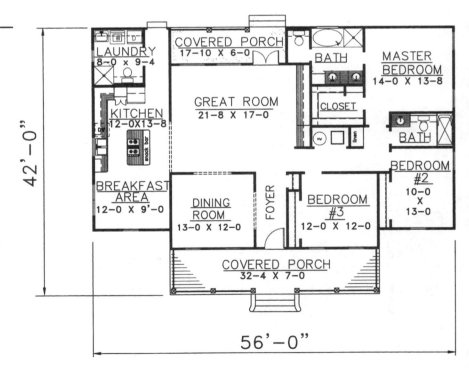

Farmhouse Style Is Inviting

Special features

- 2,340 total square feet of living area
- Large family room has vaulted ceiling, bookcases and an entertainment center which surrounds a brick fireplace
- Highly functional kitchen is easily accessible from many parts of this home
- The second floor consists of two secondary bedrooms each having direct access to the bath
- The loft can serve as a recreation area or fifth bedroom
- 3 bedrooms, 2 1/2 baths, 2-car side entry garage
- Walk-out basement foundation
- 1,689 square feet on the first floor and 651 square feet on the second floor

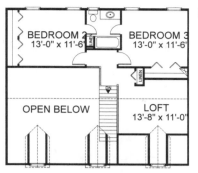

Second Floor

BEDROOM 2
13'-0" x 11'-6"

BEDROOM 3
13'-0" x 11'-6"

OPEN BELOW

LOFT
13'-8" x 11'-0"

First Floor

DECK
35'-8" x 11'-7"

STORAGE
9'-10" x 6'-0"

PANTRY

LAUNDRY
11'-6" x 6'-0"

BRKFST
9'-5" x 11'-6"

KITCHEN
12'-4" x 11'-6"

DINING
13'-8" x 11'-6"

HERS

HIS

GARAGE
21'-8" x 21'-0"

FAMILY
18'-2" x 19'-6"

STAIRS TO BASEMENT

K/S

VAULT

COATS

OFFICE/
BEDROOM
13'-8" x 11'-0"

TRAY CEILING

MASTER BDRM
15'-8" x 14'-10"

OPEN TO DORMERS

UP

PORCH

◄ 74'-4' ►

39'-4"
+DECK

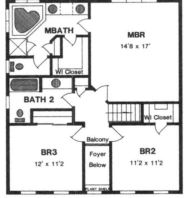

Second Floor

MBATH

MBR
14'8 x 17'

WI Closet

BATH 2

WI Closet

Balcony

BR3
12' x 11'2

Foyer
Below

BR2
11'2 x 11'2

PLANT SHELF

PANTRY

DIN
10'6 x 11'8

DESK

GREAT RM
15'8 x 17'

STOVE

KIT
12'3 x 11'

REF

Width: 52'-2"
Depth: 40'-0"

First Floor

Entry

DIN RM
11'10 x 12'

Two-Story
FOYER

Lav

Laun

GARAGE
23'4 x 23'4

Covered Entry

Enhanced By Columned Porch

Special features

- 1,887 total square feet of living area
- Enormous great room is the heart of this home with an overlooking kitchen and dining room
- Formal dining room has lovely bay window
- Master bedroom has spacious bath with corner step-up tub, double vanity and walk-in closet
- 3 bedrooms, 2 1/2 baths, 2-car garage
- Basement foundation
- 961 square feet on the first floor and 926 square feet on the second floor

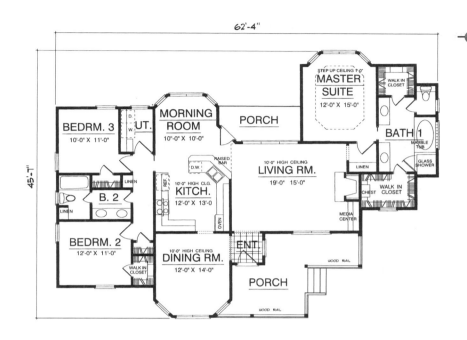

Easy Living
Special features

- 1,753 total square feet of living area
- Large front porch has charming appeal
- Kitchen with breakfast bar overlooks morning room and accesses covered porch
- Master suite with amenities like private bath, spacious closets and sunny bay window
- 3 bedrooms, 2 baths
- Slab or crawl space foundation, please specify when ordering

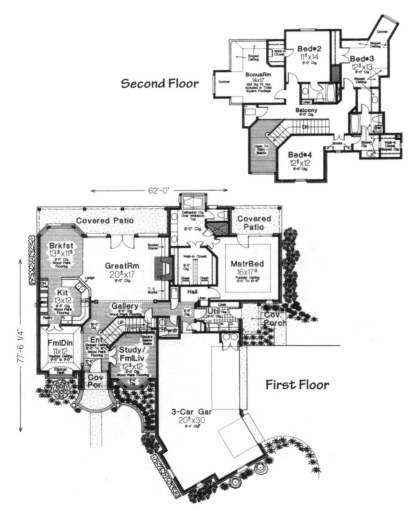

Second Floor

First Floor

Private First Floor Master Suite

Special features

- 3,017 total square feet of living area
- Impressive two-story entry has curved staircase
- Family room has unique elliptical vault above window
- Master suite includes a private covered patio and bath with walk-in closet
- Breakfast area overlooks great room
- Bonus room has an additional 234 square feet of living area
- 4 bedrooms, 3 1/2 baths, 3-car side entry garage
- Slab foundation
- 2,039 square feet on the first floor and 978 square feet on the second floor

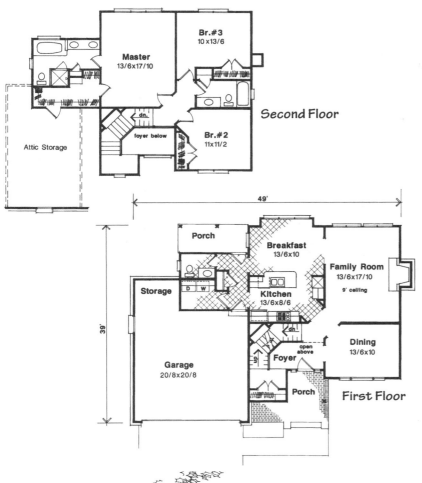

Second Floor

- Master 13/6x17/10
- Br.#3 10x13/6
- Attic Storage
- Br.#2 11x11/2
- dn.
- foyer below

First Floor

- 49'
- 39'
- Porch
- Breakfast 13/6x10
- Family Room 13/6x17/10
- 9' ceiling
- Storage
- D W
- Kitchen 13/6x8/6
- dn
- Garage 20/8x20/8
- up
- Foyer
- open above
- Dining 13/6x10
- Porch

Unique Angled Stairs

Special features

- 1,855 total square feet of living area
- Angled stairs add character to the two-story foyer
- Secluded dining area is formal and elegant
- Sunny master bedroom has all the luxuries
- A half bath is conveniently located off the kitchen and breakfast area
- 3 bedrooms, 2 1/2 baths, 2-car garage
- Basement foundation
- 990 square feet on the first floor and 865 square feet on the second floor

Multiple See-Through Fireplaces

Special features

- 2,900 total square feet of living area

- Stately arched entry with double-doors is inviting to guests

- Decorative columns through entry, dining area and great room add look of elegance

- Octagon-shaped breakfast room with intricate tray ceiling looks out to screened-in porch and large rear deck

- 9' ceilings in bedrooms and kitchen area

- 2 bedrooms, 2 1/2 baths, 2-car garage with golf cart storage

- Walk-out basement or basement foundation, please specify when ordering

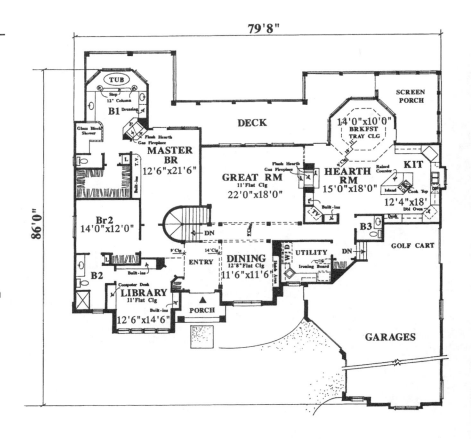

Second Floor

50'0"

44'0"

First Floor

Graceful Southern Hospitality

Special features

- 1,771 total square feet of living area
- Efficient country kitchen shares space with a bayed eating area
- Two-story family/great room is warmed by a fireplace in winter and open to outdoor country comfort in the summer with double French doors
- First floor master suite offers a bay window and access to the porch through French doors
- 3 bedrooms, 2 1/2 baths, optional detached 2-car garage
- Basement foundation
- 1,171 square feet on the first floor and 600 square feet on the second floor

Spacious One-Story With French Country Flavor

Special features

- 2,695 total square feet of living area

- A grandscale great room features a fireplace with flanking shelves, handsome entry foyer with staircase and opens to large kitchen and breakfast room

- Roomy master bedroom has a bay window, huge walk-in closet and bath with a shower built for two

- Bedrooms #2 and #3 are generously oversized with walk-in closets and a Jack and Jill style bath

- 3 bedrooms, 2 1/2 baths, 2-car side entry garage

- Basement foundation

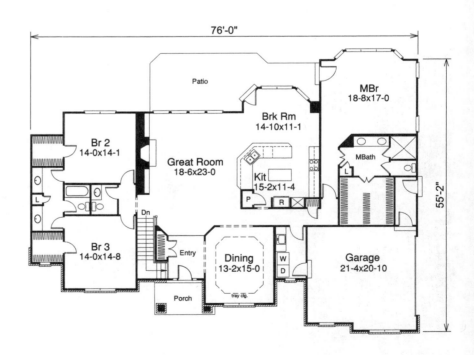

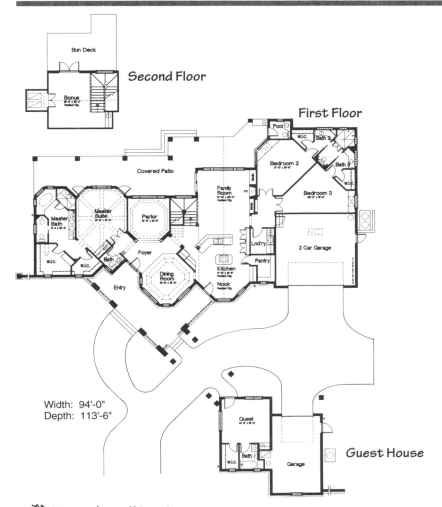

Second Floor

First Floor

Guest House

Width: 94'-0"
Depth: 113'-6"

Quiet Retreat In Parlor

Special features

- 3,436 total square feet of living area
- Unique angled rooms create exciting feel
- Well-organized kitchen with island is adjacent to family room
- Beautiful sculptured ceilings in master suite
- Guest house is ideal as in-law suite or secluded home office
- 4 bedrooms, 4 baths, 2-car and 1-car garage
- Slab foundation
- 2,816 square feet on the first floor, 290 square feet on the second floor and 330 square feet in the guest house

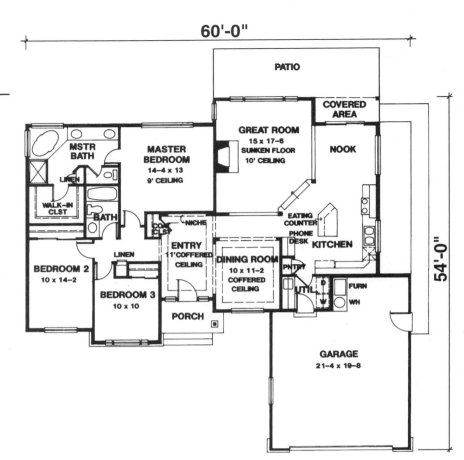

Bedrooms Separated From Living Areas

Special features

- 1,734 total square feet of living area
- Large entry with coffered ceiling and display niches
- Sunken great room has 10' ceiling
- Kitchen island includes eating counter
- 9' ceiling in master bedroom
- Master bath features corner tub and double sinks
- 3 bedrooms, 2 baths, 2-car garage
- Crawl space foundation

Plan #X26-DR-2940

Price Code A

Comfortable Home Has Character

Special features

- 1,482 total square feet of living area
- Energy efficient home with 2" x 6" exterior walls
- Corner fireplace warms living area
- Screened is spacious and connects to other living areas in the home
- Two bedrooms on second floor share a spacious bath
- 2 bedrooms, 1 1/2 baths
- Basement foundation
- 895 square feet on the first floor and 587 square feet on the second floor

Second Floor

First Floor

Raised Foyer And Living Room

Special features

- 2,221 total square feet of living area
- Master bedroom is open, airy and well-located
- Family room has 12' wall of sliding glass doors bringing the outdoors in
- Separate secondary bedrooms for privacy
- 4 bedrooms, 3 baths, 2-car garage
- Slab foundation

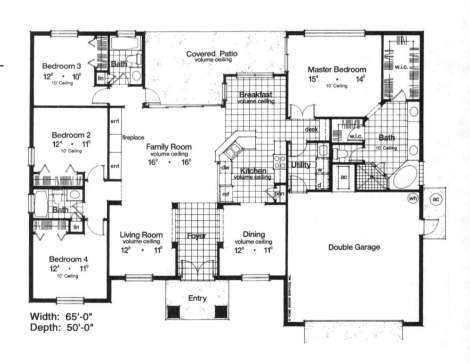

Width: 65'-0"
Depth: 50'-0"

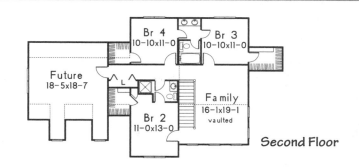

Second Floor

Cozy Country-Style Home

Special features

- 2,795 total square feet of living area
- Second floor has cozy vaulted family room
- Formal dining room directly off kitchen
- Spacious great room with fireplace has built-in entertainment center
- Bonus room has 387 square feet of additional living area
- 4 bedrooms, 3 1/2 baths, 2-car side entry garage
- Basement foundation, drawings also include crawl space or slab foundation
- 1,787 square feet on the first floor and 1,008 square feet on the second floor

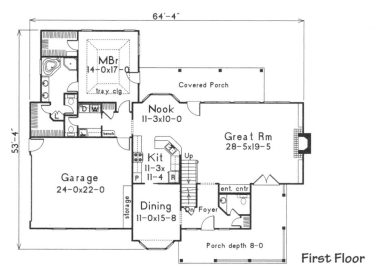

First Floor

Island Work Space

Special features

- 1,464 total square feet of living area
- Contemporary styled home has breathtaking two-story foyer and lovely open staircase
- Efficiently designed U-shaped kitchen
- Elegant great room has a cozy fireplace
- 3 bedrooms, 2 1/2 baths, 2-car garage
- Crawl space foundation
- 655 square feet on the first floor and 809 square feet on the second floor

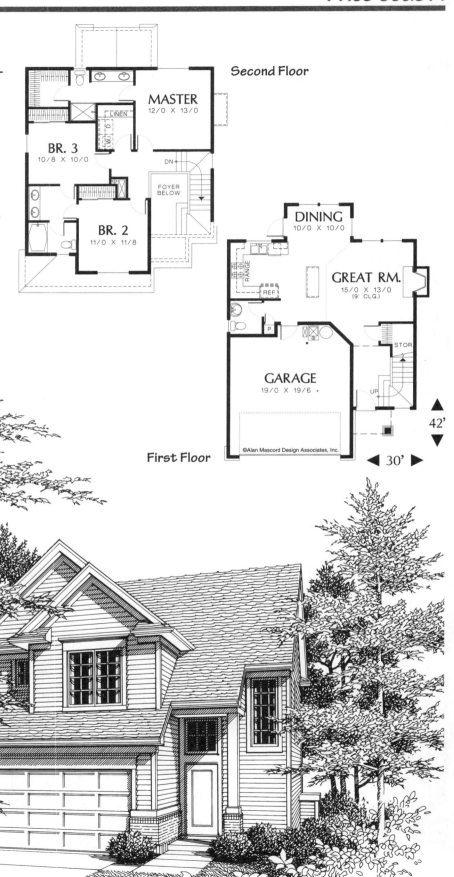

Second Floor

MASTER
12/0 X 13/0

LINEN

BR. 3
10/8 X 10/0

DN

FOYER
BELOW

BR. 2
11/0 X 11/8

DINING
10/0 X 10/0

GREAT RM.
15/0 X 13/0
(9' CLG.)

RANGE

REF

P.

STOR

GARAGE
19/0 X 19/6 +

UP

©Alan Mascord Design Associates, Inc.

First Floor

42'

30'

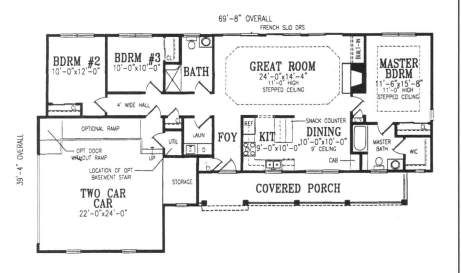

Modest Farmhouse Ranch

Special features

- 1,480 total square feet of living area

- Split bedroom floor plan with private master suite includes large bath and walk-in closet

- Fabulous great room features 11' high step ceiling, fireplace and media center

- Floor plan designed to be fully accessible for handicapped

- 3 bedrooms, 2 baths, 2-car side entry garage

- Basement, crawl space or slab foundation, please specify when ordering foundation

Beautiful
Country Victorian

Special features

- 1,760 total square feet of living area
- Unfinished space above garage ideal for future expansion
- 9' ceiling on first floor
- Energy efficient home with 2" x 6" exterior walls
- 3 bedrooms, 2 1/2 baths, 1-car garage
- Basement foundation
- 880 square feet on the first floor and 880 square feet on the second floor

Second Floor

4,00 X 2,70
13'-4" X 9'-0"

3,30 X 3,30
11'-0" X 11'-0"

BONUS ROOM
4,70 X 4,60
15'-8" X 15'-4"

3,80 X 4,70
12'-8" X 15'-8"

First Floor

6,20 X 3,40
20'-8" X 11'-4"

5,10 X 3,30
17'-0" X 11'-0"

4,60 X 6,80
15'-4" X 22'-8"

3,80 X 4,70
12'-8" X 15'-8"

12,0 m
40'-0"

12,6 m
42'-0"

Angles
Add Interest

Special features

- 2,201 total square feet of living area
- Open floor plan makes home feel airy and bright
- Beautiful living room has cheerful bay window
- Master suite has his/her walk-in closets
- Family room, kitchen and breakfast area combine for added space
- 3 bedrooms, 2 1/2 baths, 2-car garage
- Walk-out basement or crawl space foundation, please specify when ordering

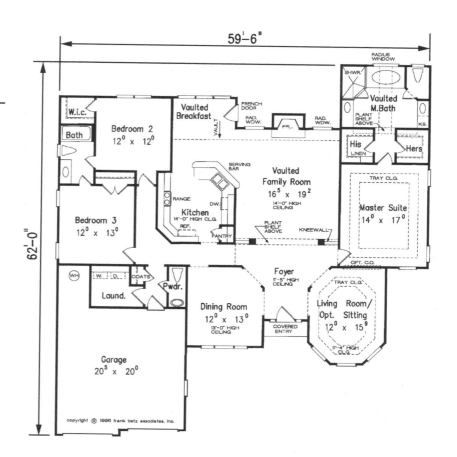

Efficiently Designed Computer Room

Special features

- 2,726 total square feet of living area
- Angled sink area with snack bar define the kitchen area
- Graceful arched accent the entry, dining room and sun room of this home
- Great room features a fireplace wrapped by cabinets for storage and has French doors leading to the covered rear porch
- 4 bedrooms, 3 1/2 baths, 2-car side entry garage
- Basement, crawl space or slab foundation, please specify when ordering

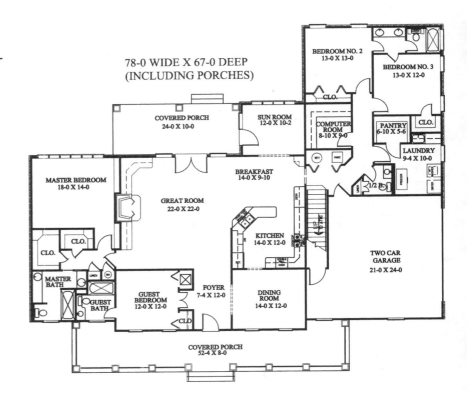

78-0 WIDE X 67-0 DEEP
(INCLUDING PORCHES)

Second Floor

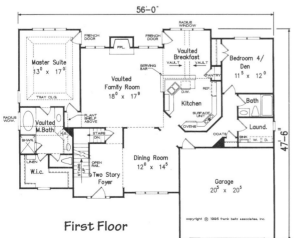

First Floor

Bright And Beautiful

Special features

- 2,349 total square feet of living area
- Open and airy with two-story foyer and family room
- Den is secluded from the rest of the home and ideal as an office space
- Second floor bedrooms have walk-in closets and share a bath
- Optional bonus room has an additional 276 square feet of living area
- 4 bedrooms, 3 baths, 2-car garage
- Walk-out basement or crawl space foundation, please specify when ordering
- 1,761 square feet on the first floor and 588 square feet on the second floor

Unique, Traditional Style, Farmhouse Flavor

Special features

- 1,763 total square feet of living area
- Dining room has a large box-bay window and a recessed ceiling
- Living room includes a large fireplace
- Kitchen has plenty of workspace, a pantry and a double sink overlooking the deck
- Master suite features a large bath with walk-in closet
- 3 bedrooms, 2 1/2 baths, 2-car garage
- Basement foundation, drawings also include crawl space and slab foundations
- 909 square feet on the first floor and 854 square feet on the second floor

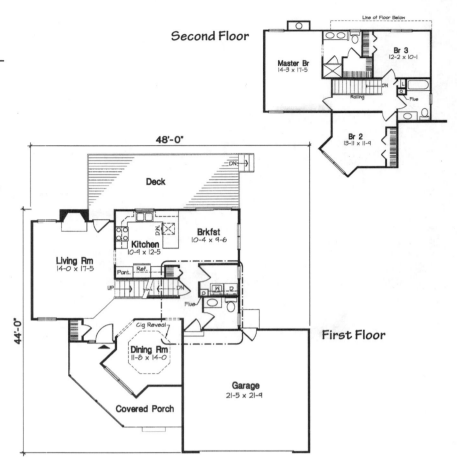

Second Floor

Master Br 14-3 x 17-5

Br 3 12-2 x 10-1

Br 2 13-11 x 11-9

First Floor

48'-0"

44'-0"

Deck

Living Rm 14-0 x 17-5

Kitchen 10-4 x 12-5

Brkfst 10-4 x 9-6

Pant.   Ref.

Dining Rm 11-8 x 14-0

Garage 21-5 x 21-4

Covered Porch

Rear View

Rooflines
Add Interest

Special features

- 1,828 total square feet of living area
- Energy efficient home with 2" x 6" exterior walls
- Master bath features a giant walk-in closet, built-in linen storage with convenient access to utility room
- Kitchen has a unique design that is elegant and practical
- 4 bedrooms, 2 baths, 2-car garage
- Slab, crawl space or basement foundation, please specify when ordering

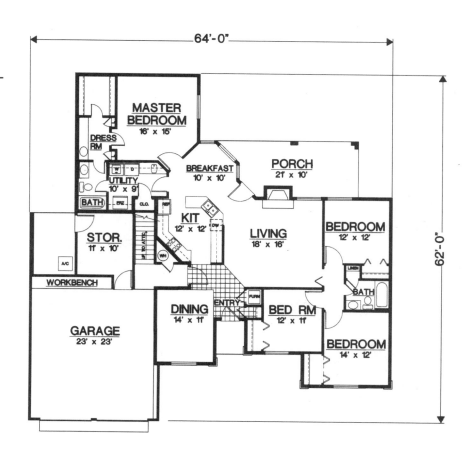

COPYRIGHT LARRY E. BELK

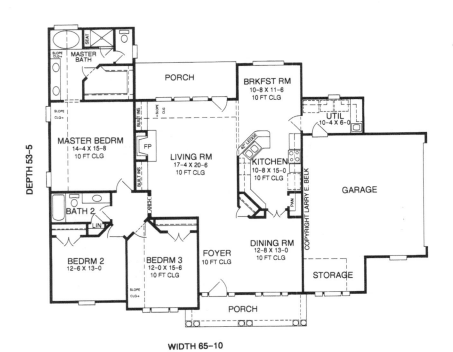

DEPTH 53-5

MASTER
BATH

PORCH

BRKFST RM
10-8 X 11-6
10 FT CLG

UTIL
10-4 X 6-0

MASTER BEDRM
14-4 X 15-8
10 FT CLG

FP

LIVING RM
17-4 X 20-6
10 FT CLG

KITCHEN
10-8 X 15-0
10 FT CLG

GARAGE

BATH 2

LIN

BEDRM 2
12-6 X 13-0

BEDRM 3
12-0 X 15-6
10 FT CLG

FOYER
10 FT CLG

DINING RM
12-8 X 13-0
10 FT CLG

COPYRIGHT LARRY E. BELK

STORAGE

PORCH

WIDTH 65-10

Circle-Top Details
Special features

- 1,932 total square feet of living area
- Double arches form entrance to this elegantly styled home
- Two palladian windows add distinction to facade
- Kitchen has angled eating bar opening to the breakfast and living rooms
- 3 bedrooms, 2 baths, 2-car side entry garage
- Crawl space or slab foundation, please specify when ordering

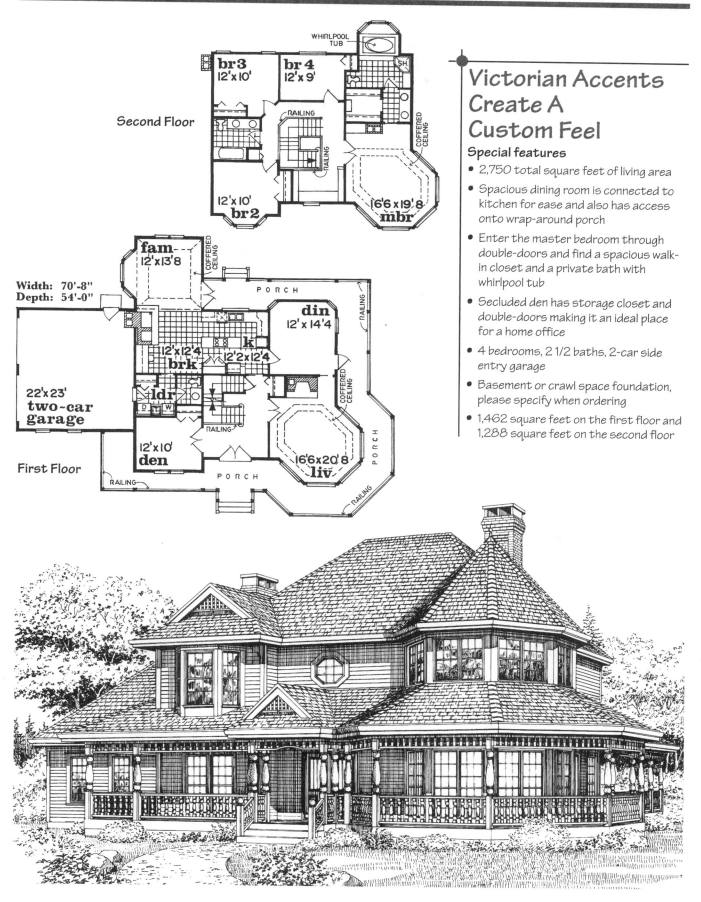

Second Floor

br3 12'x10'
br 4 12'x9'
WHIRLPOOL TUB
RAILING
COFFERED CEILING
SH
RAILING
12'x10' br2
16'6 x 19'8 mbr

Width: 70'-8"
Depth: 54'-0"

fam 12'x13'8
COFFERED CEILING
PORCH
din 12'x14'4
RAILING
COFFERED CEILING
12'x12'4 brk
k
12'2x12'4
COFFERED CEILING
22'x23' two-car garage
ldr
D W
RAILING
12'x10' den
RAILING
PORCH
16'6 x20'8 liv
PORCH
RAILING

First Floor

Victorian Accents Create A Custom Feel

Special features

- 2,750 total square feet of living area
- Spacious dining room is connected to kitchen for ease and also has access onto wrap-around porch
- Enter the master bedroom through double-doors and find a spacious walk-in closet and a private bath with whirlpool tub
- Secluded den has storage closet and double-doors making it an ideal place for a home office
- 4 bedrooms, 2 1/2 baths, 2-car side entry garage
- Basement or crawl space foundation, please specify when ordering
- 1,462 square feet on the first floor and 1,288 square feet on the second floor

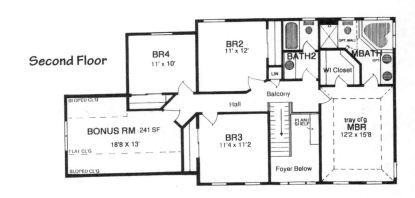

Second Floor

BR4
11' x 10'

BR2
11' x 12'

BATH2

MBATH

OPT.WALL

OPT

LIN

WI Closet

SLOPED CL'G

Balcony

Hall

PLANT SHELF

tray cl'g
MBR
12'2 x 15'8

BONUS RM 241 SF
18'8 X 13'

FLAT CL'G

BR3
11'4 x 11'2

Foyer Below

SLOPED CL'G

Bright And Cheery Sun Room

Special features

- 2,211 total square feet of living area
- Spacious sun room has three walls of windows and access outdoors
- Family room has open view into kitchen and dining area
- Large master bedroom has private luxurious bath with step-up tub
- Bonus room has an additional 241 square feet of living area
- 4 bedrooms, 2 1/2 baths, 2-car garage
- Basement foundation
- 1,189 square feet on the first floor and 1,022 square feet on the second floor

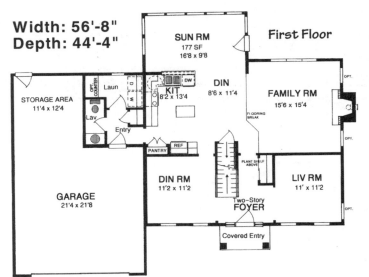

Width: 56'-8"
Depth: 44'-4"

First Floor

SUN RM
177 SF
16'8 x 9'8

DIN
8'6 x 11'4

FAMILY RM
15'6 x 15'4

STORAGE AREA
11'4 x 12'4

OPT. COUNTER

Laun

KIT
8'2 x 13'4

DW

FLOORING BREAK

Lav

Entry

PANTRY

REF

PLANT SHELF ABOVE

DIN RM
11'2 x 11'2

LIV RM
11' x 11'2

GARAGE
21'4 x 21'8

Two-Story
FOYER

Covered Entry

M. MAXON

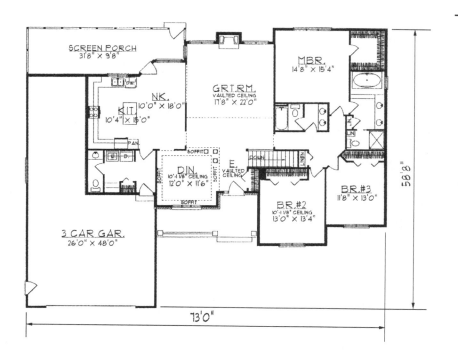

SCREEN PORCH
31'8" x 3'8"

NK.
10'0" x 18'0"

KIT
10'4" x 15'0"

GRT. RM.
VAULTED CEILING
17'8" x 22'0"

M.B.R.
14'8" x 15'4"

PAN

DIN
10'-1 1/8" CEILING
12'0" x 11'6"

E.
VAULTED
CEILING

SOFFIT

SOFFIT

SOFFIT

CL.

LINEN

LIN

B.R. #2
10'-1 1/8" CEILING
13'0" x 13'4"

B.R. #3
11'8" x 13'0"

3 CAR GAR.
26'0" x 48'0"

58'8"

73'0"

Luxurious Ranch
Special features
- 2,196 total square feet of living area
- Covered front porch leads to the vaulted foyer which invites guests into the great room
- Master bedroom features walk-in closet, private bath with double vanity, spa tub and linen closet
- Large open kitchen
- 3 bedrooms, 2 1/2 baths, 3-car garage
- Basement foundation

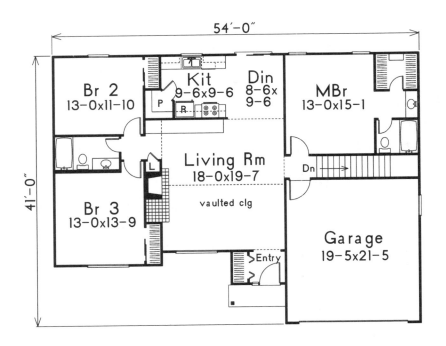

Spacious Living In This Ranch

Special features

- 1,433 total square feet of living area
- Vaulted living room includes cozy fireplace and an oversized entertainment center
- Bedrooms #2 and #3 share a full bath
- Master bedroom has a full bath and large walk-in closet
- 3 bedrooms, 2 baths, 2-car garage
- Basement foundation, drawings also include crawl space and slab foundations

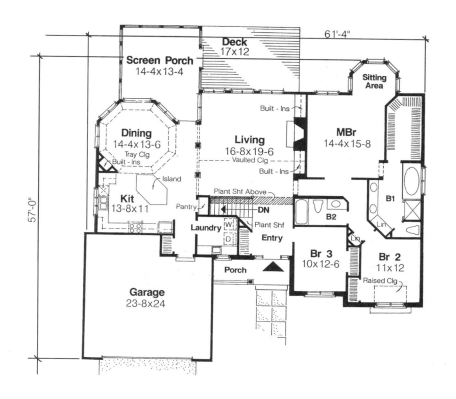

Pleasant Screened Porch

Special features

- 2,003 total square feet of living area
- Living room has a relaxing feel with center fireplace surrounded by built-in cabinets, vaulted ceiling and sunny wall of windows allowing view to the outdoors
- Master bedroom features sunny octagon-shaped sitting area perfect for quiet time
- 9' ceiling throughout this home
- 3 bedrooms, 2 baths, 2-car garage
- Basement foundation

© Urban Design Group, Inc.

A Welcoming Farmhouse Style

Special features

- 2,743 total square feet of living area
- 9' ceilings on first floor of this home
- Kitchen, breakfast and hearth rooms connect creating one large living space ideal for family living
- Master suite has its own wing with large private bath and walk-in closet
- Wrap-around porch in the front of the home makes a lasting impression
- 3 bedrooms, 2 1/2 baths, 2-car garage
- Slab foundation
- 2,153 square feet on the first floor and 590 square feet on the second floor

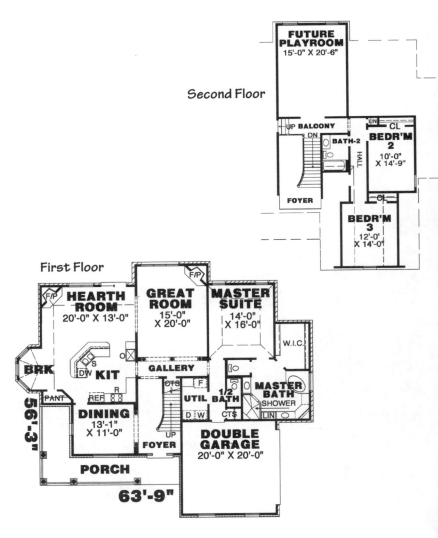

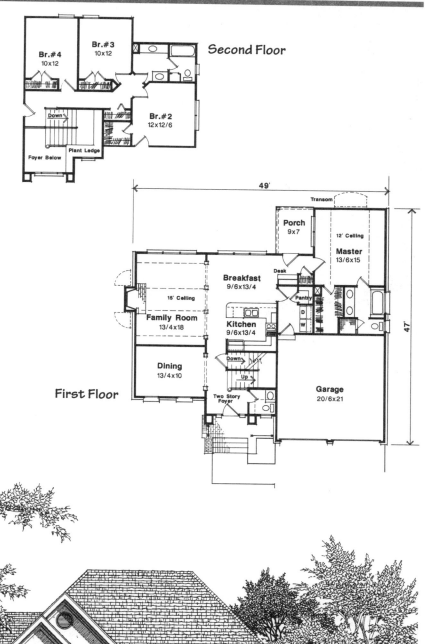

Plant Ledge
Accents Foyer

Special features

- 2,008 total square feet of living area
- Family room has character with 15' ceiling, fireplace and columns separating it from breakfast/kitchen area
- Inviting two-story foyer with plant shelves
- Private master suite enjoys porch views
- 4 bedrooms, 2 1/2 baths, 2-car garage
- Basement foundation
- 1,318 square feet on the first floor and 690 square feet on the second floor

Width: 85'-0"
Depth: 85'-0"

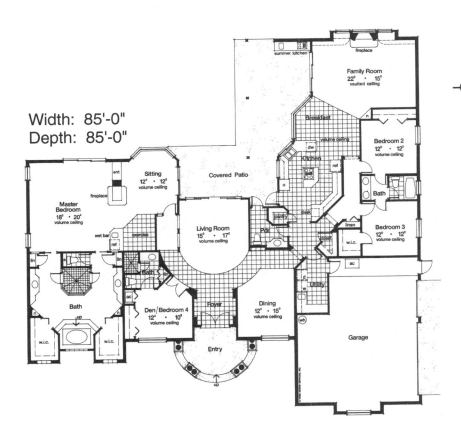

Enormous Master Bath

Special features

- 3,556 total square feet of living area
- Curved portico welcomes guests
- Master suite has see-through fire-place, wet bar, private bath and sitting area opening to covered patio
- Cozy family room with fireplace has adjacent summer kitchen outdoors on patio
- 4 bedrooms, 3 1/2 baths, 3-car side entry garage
- Slab foundation

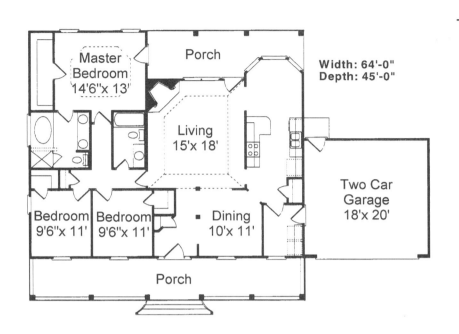

Width: 64'-0"
Depth: 45'-0"

Full-Length Front Porch

Special features

- 1,500 total square feet of living area
- Living room features corner fireplace adding warmth
- Master suite has all the amenities like walk-in closet, private bath and porch access
- Sunny bayed breakfast room is cheerful and bright
- 3 bedrooms, 2 baths, 2-car garage
- Slab foundation

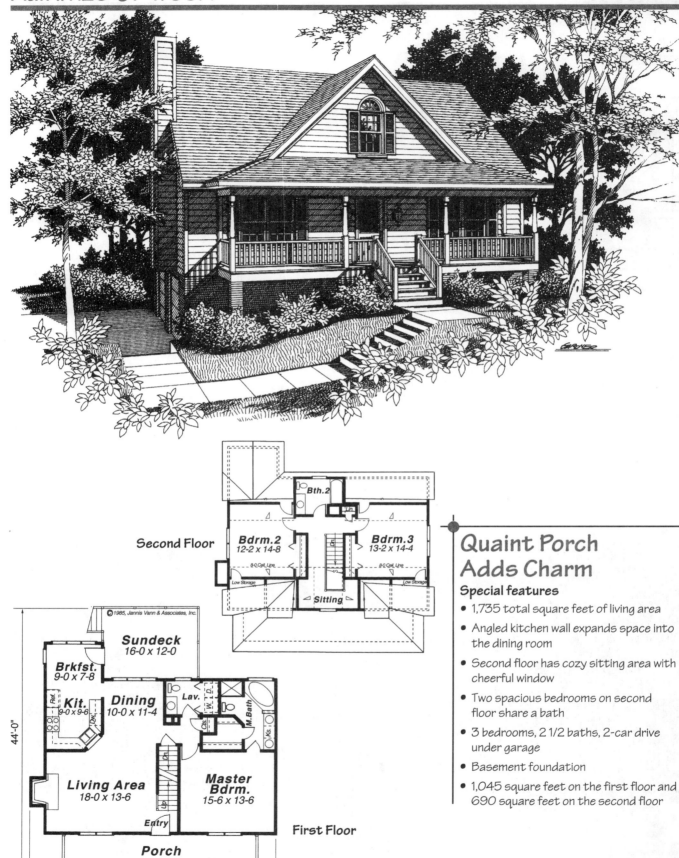

Second Floor

Bth.2

Bdrm.2
12-2 x 14-8

Bdrm.3
13-2 x 14-4

Low Storage   Low Storage

Sitting

© 1985, Jannis Vann & Associates, Inc.

Sundeck
16-0 x 12-0

Brkfst.
9-0 x 7-8

Ref.

Kit.
9-0 x 9-6

Dw.

Dining
10-0 x 11-4

Lav.

W. D.

Cls.

M. Bath.

Ws.

Living Area
18-0 x 13-6

Master Bdrm.
15-6 x 13-6

Entry

44'-0"

40'-4"

Porch

First Floor

Quaint Porch Adds Charm

Special features

- 1,735 total square feet of living area
- Angled kitchen wall expands space into the dining room
- Second floor has cozy sitting area with cheerful window
- Two spacious bedrooms on second floor share a bath
- 3 bedrooms, 2 1/2 baths, 2-car drive under garage
- Basement foundation
- 1,045 square feet on the first floor and 690 square feet on the second floor

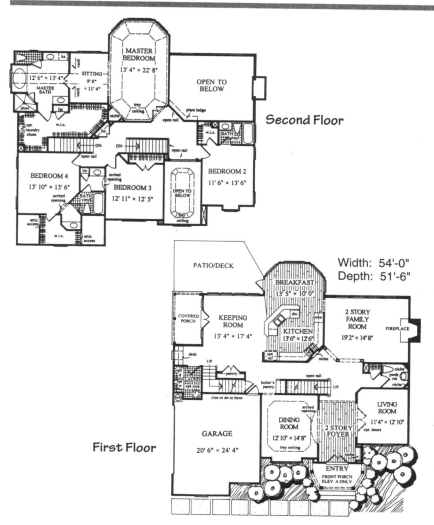

Second Floor

MASTER BEDROOM 13' 4" × 22' 8"

SITTING 9' 0" × 11' 4"

12' 6" × 13' 4" MASTER BATH

OPEN TO BELOW

BEDROOM 4 13' 10" × 13' 6"

BEDROOM 3 12' 11" × 12' 5"

OPEN TO BELOW

BEDROOM 2 11' 6" × 13' 6"

First Floor

Width: 54'-0"
Depth: 51'-6"

PATIO/DECK

BREAKFAST 13' 5" × 10' 0"

COVERED PORCH

KEEPING ROOM 13' 4" × 17' 4"

KITCHEN 13' 6" × 12' 6"

2 STORY FAMILY ROOM 19' 2" × 14' 8"

FIREPLACE

GARAGE 20' 6" × 24' 4"

DINING ROOM 12' 10" × 14' 8"

2 STORY FOYER

LIVING ROOM 11' 4" × 12' 10"

ENTRY
FRONT PORCH ELEV. A ONLY

Luxurious Home, Inside And Out

Special features

- 3,422 total square feet of living area
- Tudor influenced brick and stucco exterior
- Arched openings in dining and living rooms
- Kitchen open to keeping room
- Convenient front and rear stairs
- Two-story family room has fireplace and balcony on second floor
- 4 bedrooms, 3 1/2 baths, 2-car side entry garage
- Basement foundation
- 1,723 square feet on the first floor and 1,699 square feet on the second floor

An Open Feel With Vaulted Ceilings

Special features

- 1,470 total square feet of living area
- Vaulted breakfast room is cheerful and sunny
- Private second floor master bedroom with bath and walk-in closet
- Large utility room has access to the outdoors
- 3 bedrooms, 2 baths
- Basement, crawl space or slab foundation, please specify when ordering
- 1,035 square feet on the first floor and 435 square feet on the second floor

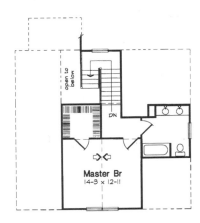

Second Floor

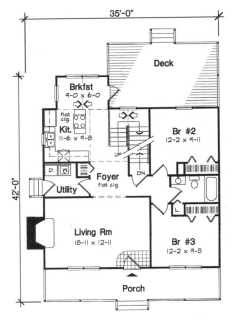

First Floor

Rear View

Second Floor

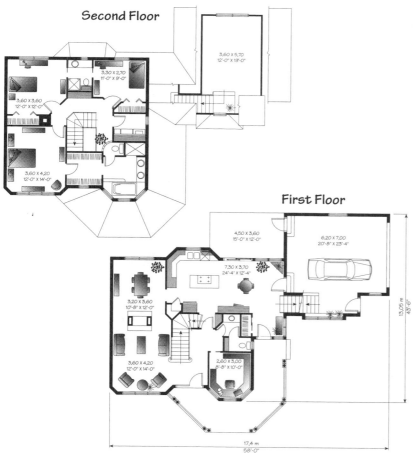

3,30 X 2,70
11'-0" X 9'-0"

3,60 X 5,70
12'-0" X 19'-0"

3,60 X 3,60
12'-0" X 12'-0"

3,60 X 4,20
12'-0" X 14'-0"

First Floor

4,50 X 3,60
15'-0" X 12'-0"

6,20 X 7,00
20'-8" X 23'-4"

7,30 X 3,70
24'-4" X 12'-0"

3,20 X 3,60
10'-8" X 12'-0"

3,60 X 4,20
12'-0" X 14'-0"

2,60 X 3,00
8'-8" X 10'-0"

13,05 m
43'-6"

17,4 m
58'-0"

Stone Highlights This Victorian Home

Special features

- 1,938 total square feet of living area
- Cozy office space on first floor
- 9' ceiling on first floor
- Energy efficient home with 2" x 6" exterior walls
- 3 bedrooms, 2 1/2 baths, 2-car side entry garage
- Basement foundation
- 1,044 square feet on the first floor and 894 square feet on the second floor

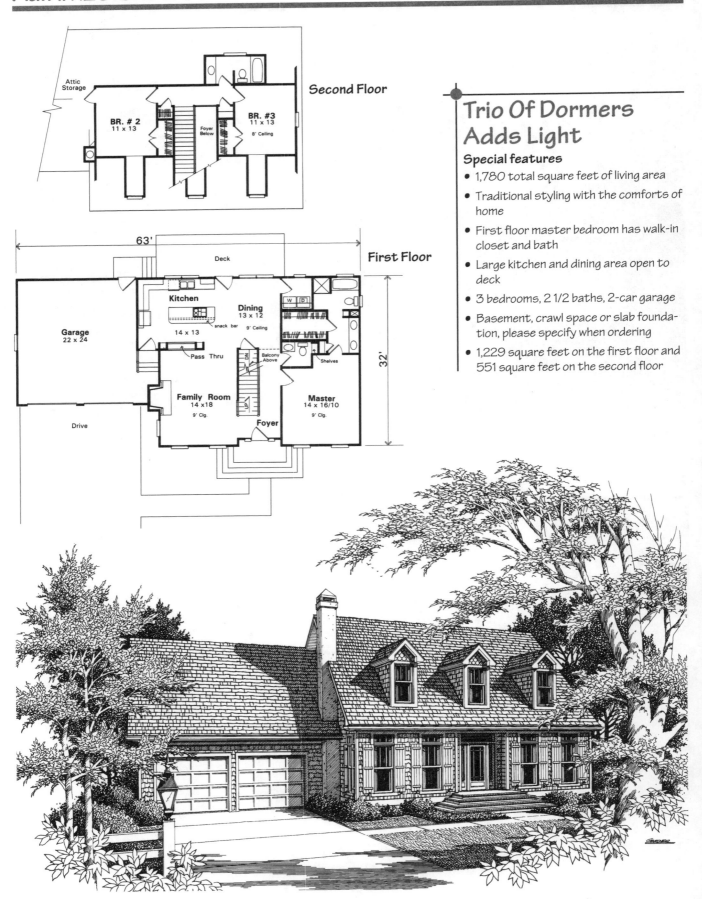

Second Floor

Attic Storage

BR. # 2
11 x 13

Foyer Below

BR. #3
11 x 13
8' Ceiling

63'

Deck

First Floor

Kitchen
14 x 13

Dining
13 x 12
9' Ceiling

Garage
22 x 24

snack bar

W D

Pass Thru

Balcony Above

Shelves

32'

Family Room
14 x18
9' Clg.

DN

UP

Master
14 x 16/10
9' Clg.

Foyer

Drive

Trio Of Dormers Adds Light

Special features

- 1,780 total square feet of living area
- Traditional styling with the comforts of home
- First floor master bedroom has walk-in closet and bath
- Large kitchen and dining area open to deck
- 3 bedrooms, 2 1/2 baths, 2-car garage
- Basement, crawl space or slab foundation, please specify when ordering
- 1,229 square feet on the first floor and 551 square feet on the second floor

Width: 58'-6"
Depth: 72'-0"

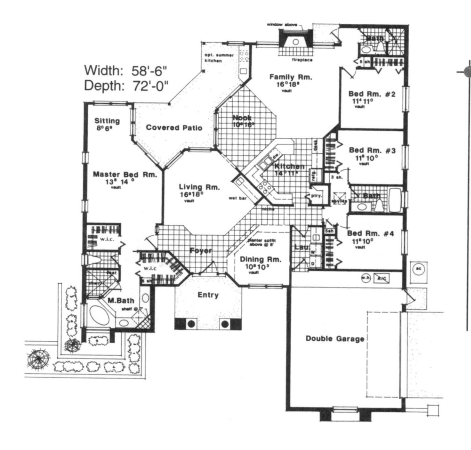

Distinctive
Angled Rooms

Special features

- 2,224 total square feet of living area

- Vaulted living room with wet bar

- Pass-through kitchen with V-shaped counter and walk-in pantry overlooks family room

- Master suite with sitting area, two walk-in closets and a full bath with tub surrounded by windows

- 4 bedrooms, 3 baths, 2-car side entry garage

- Slab foundation

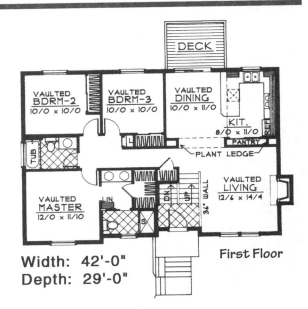

Width: 42'-0"
Depth: 29'-0"

First Floor

Split-Level With A Country Feel

Special features

- 1,742 total square feet of living area
- Vaulted rooms create a spacious feel throughout this plan
- U-shaped kitchen is efficiently designed to have everything within reach
- Lower level includes additional space for future expansion
- 3 bedrooms, 2 baths, 2-car garage
- Basement foundation
- 1,183 square feet on the first floor and 559 square feet on the lower level

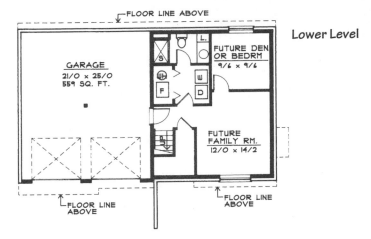

Lower Level

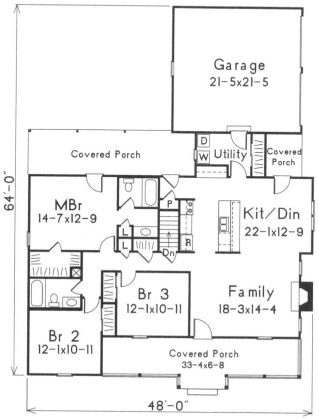

Garage
21-5x21-5

Covered Porch

D
W Utility

Covered Porch

MBr
14-7x12-9

Kit/Din
22-1x12-9

P

L
L

Dn
R

Br 3
12-1x10-11

Family
18-3x14-4

Br 2
12-1x10-11

Covered Porch
33-4x6-8

64'-0"

48'-0"

Country-Style Home With Large Front Porch

Special features

- 1,501 total square feet of living area
- Spacious kitchen with dining area is open to the outdoors
- Convenient utility room is adjacent to garage
- Master suite with private bath, dressing area and access to large covered porch
- Large family room creates openness
- 3 bedrooms, 2 baths, 2-car side entry garage
- Basement foundation, drawings also include crawl space and slab foundations

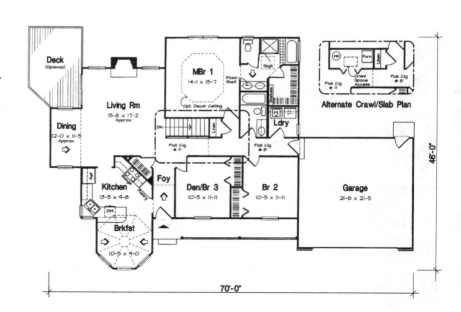

Handsome Octagon-Shaped Breakfast Room

Special features

- 1,583 total square feet of living area
- Dining area is open to living room making a terrific gathering place
- Cheerful skylight in private master bath
- Living room has center fireplace creating a cozy atmosphere
- 3 bedrooms, 2 baths, 2-car garage
- Basement, crawl space or slab foundation, please specify when ordering

© COPYRIGHT 1990 RALPH JONES & ASSOC.

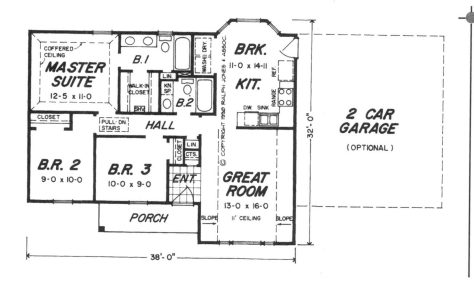

Arched Window Is A Focal Point

Special features

- 1,021 total square feet of living area
- 11' ceiling in great room expands living area
- Combination kitchen/breakfast room allows for easy preparation and cleanup
- Master suite features private bath and oversized walk-in closet
- 3 bedrooms, 2 baths, optional 2-car garage
- Slab or crawl space foundation, please specify when ordering

Grand Living Area

Special features

- 2,788 total square feet of living area

- Georgian grandeur with this elegant ranch design

- Spacious screened porch just beyond breakfast area stretches casual space to the outdoors

- A home office located conveniently off the living area could easily convert to a fourth bedroom

- 3 bedrooms, 2 1/2 baths, 2-car side entry garage

- Basement foundation

Traditional Styling

Special features

- 2,050 total square feet of living area
- Living room immersed in sunlight from wall of windows
- Master suite with amenities such as double walk-in closets, private bath and view onto covered porch
- Cozy family room features built-in shelves and a fireplace
- 3 bedrooms, 2 baths, 2-car side entry garage
- Crawl space or slab foundation, please specify when ordering

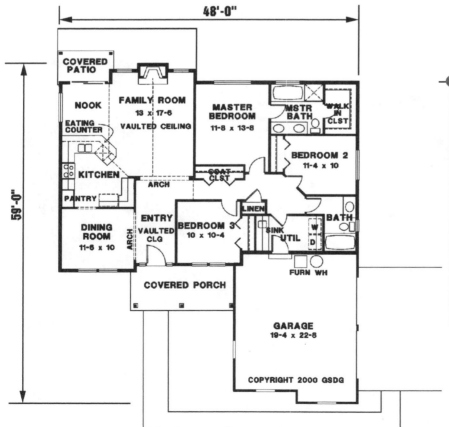

COVERED PATIO

NOOK

FAMILY ROOM
13 x 17-6
VAULTED CEILING

MASTER BEDROOM
11-8 x 13-8

MSTR BATH

WALK IN CLST

EATING COUNTER

KITCHEN

PANTRY

ARCH

COAT CLST

BEDROOM 2
11-4 x 10

DINING ROOM
11-6 x 10

ARCH

ENTRY
VAULTED CLG

BEDROOM 3
10 x 10-4

LINEN

SINK

UTIL

W D

BATH

FURN WH

COVERED PORCH

GARAGE
19-4 x 22-8

COPYRIGHT 2000 GSDG

48'-0"

59'-0"

Cottage-Style Adds Charm

Special features

- 1,496 total square feet of living area
- Large utility room with sink and extra counterspace
- Covered patio off breakfast nook extends dining to the outdoors
- Eating counter in kitchen overlooks vaulted family room
- 3 bedrooms, 2 baths, 2-car side entry garage
- Crawl space foundation

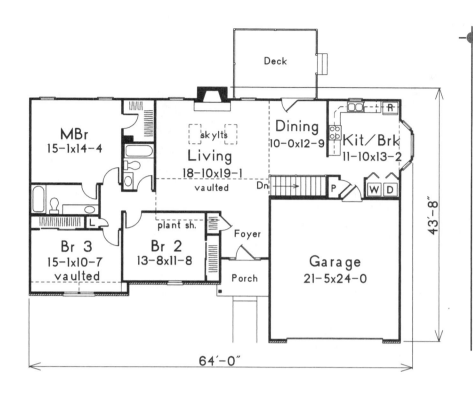

Deck

MBr
15-1x14-4

skylts

Living
18-10x19-1
vaulted

Dining
10-0x12-9

Kit/Brk
11-10x13-2

R

Dn

P

W D

Br 3
15-1x10-7
vaulted

plant sh.

Br 2
13-8x11-8

Foyer

Porch

Garage
21-5x24-0

43'-8"

64'-0"

L

Vaulted Ceilings And Light Add Dimension

Special features

- 1,676 total square feet of living area
- The living area skylights and large breakfast room with bay window provide plenty of sunlight
- The master bedroom has a walk-in closet and both the secondary bedrooms have large closets
- Vaulted ceilings, plant shelving and a fireplace provide a quality living area
- 3 bedrooms, 2 baths, 2-car garage
- Basement foundation, drawings also include crawl space and slab foundations

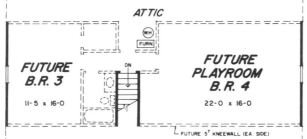

Optional Second Floor

FUTURE B.R. 3
11-5 x 16-0

ATTIC

WH
FURN

DN

FUTURE PLAYROOM B.R. 4
22-0 x 16-0

FUTURE 5' KNEEWALL (EA SIDE)

Decorative Accents Featured On Front Porch

Special features

- 1,455 total square feet of living area

- Spacious mud room has a large pantry, space for a freezer, sink/counter area and bath with shower

- Bedroom #2 can easily be converted to a study or office area

- Optional second floor bedroom and playroom have an additional 744 square feet of living space

- 2 bedrooms, 2 baths

- Slab or crawl space foundation, please specify when ordering

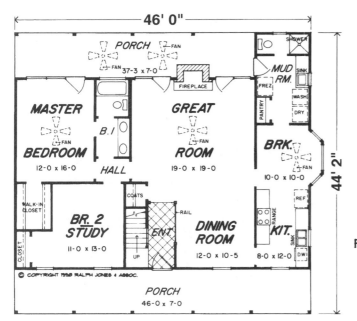

46' 0"

PORCH
37-3 x 7-0
FAN   FAN   FAN

FIREPLACE

MUD RM.
SHOWER
SINK
FREZ.
PANTRY
WASH
DRY

MASTER BEDROOM
12-0 x 16-0

B.1

GREAT ROOM
19-0 x 19-0
FAN

BRK.
10-0 x 10-0
FAN

HALL

WALK-IN CLOSET

BR. 2 STUDY
11-0 x 13-0

COATS
ENT.
RAIL

DINING ROOM
12-0 x 10-5

KIT.
8-0 x 12-0
REF
RANGE
SINK
DW

CLOSET

UP

© COPYRIGHT 1988 RALPH JONES & ASSOC.

PORCH
46-0 x 7-0

44' 2"

First Floor

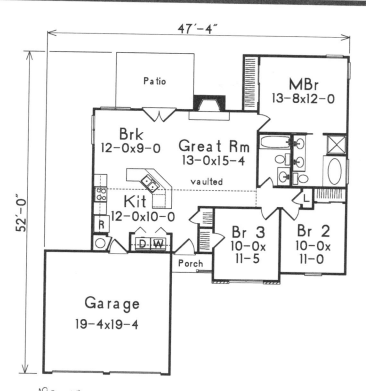

Patio

Brk
12-0x9-0

Great Rm
13-0x15-4

vaulted

MBr
13-8x12-0

Kit
12-0x10-0

D W

Br 3
10-0x
11-5

Br 2
10-0x
11-0

Porch

Garage
19-4x19-4

47'-4"

52'-0"

R

Brick And Siding Enhance This Traditional Home

Special features

- 1,170 total square feet of living area
- Master bedroom enjoys privacy at the rear of this home
- Kitchen has angled bar that overlooks great room and breakfast area
- Living areas combine to create a greater sense of spaciousness
- Great room has a cozy fireplace
- 3 bedrooms, 2 baths, 2-car garage
- Slab foundation

Country Cottage Styling

Special features

- 1,251 total square feet of living area
- Open living areas make this home feel larger
- Utility closet located on the second floor for convenience
- Lots of counterspace in kitchen
- 3 bedrooms, 2 baths, 2-car rear entry garage
- Crawl space foundation
- 792 square feet on the first floor and 459 square feet on the second floor

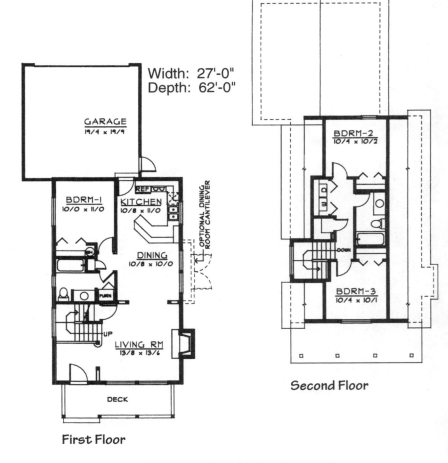

Width: 27'-0"
Depth: 62'-0"

GARAGE
19/4 x 19/9

BDRM-1
10/0 x 11/0

KITCHEN
10/8 x 11/0

REF

OPTIONAL DINING ROOM CANTILEVER

DINING
10/8 x 10/0

FURN

UP

LIVING RM
13/8 x 13/6

DECK

First Floor

BDRM-2
10/4 x 10/2

W D

DOWN

BDRM-3
10/4 x 10/1

Second Floor

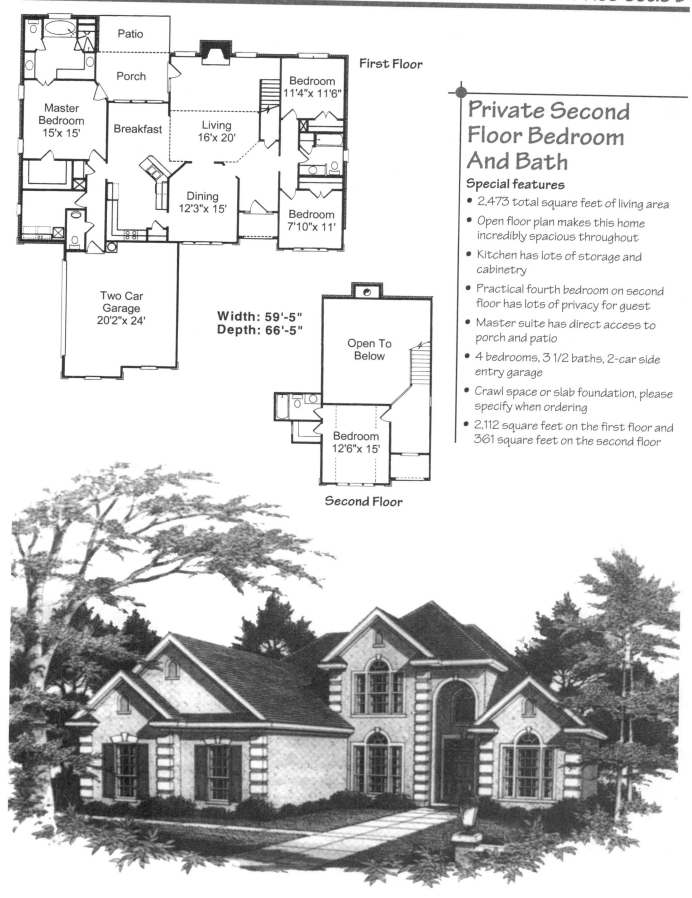

First Floor

Patio

Porch

Master Bedroom
15'x 15'

Breakfast

Living
16'x 20'

Bedroom
11'4"x 11'6"

Dining
12'3"x 15'

Bedroom
7'10"x 11'

Two Car Garage
20'2"x 24'

Width: 59'-5"
Depth: 66'-5"

Open To Below

Bedroom
12'6"x 15'

Second Floor

Private Second Floor Bedroom And Bath

Special features

- 2,473 total square feet of living area
- Open floor plan makes this home incredibly spacious throughout
- Kitchen has lots of storage and cabinetry
- Practical fourth bedroom on second floor has lots of privacy for guest
- Master suite has direct access to porch and patio
- 4 bedrooms, 3 1/2 baths, 2-car side entry garage
- Crawl space or slab foundation, please specify when ordering
- 2,112 square feet on the first floor and 361 square feet on the second floor

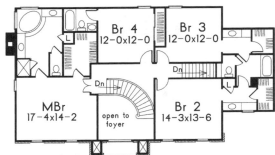

Second Floor

Two-Story Foyer With Grand Curved Stairway

Special features

- 3,144 total square feet of living area
- 9' ceilings on first floor
- Kitchen offers large pantry, island cooktop and close proximity to laundry and dining rooms
- Expansive family room includes wet bar, fireplace and attractive bay window
- 4 bedrooms, 4 1/2 baths, 3-car side entry garage
- Basement foundation
- 1,724 square feet on the first floor and 1,420 square feet on the second floor

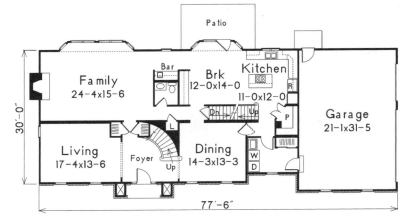

First Floor

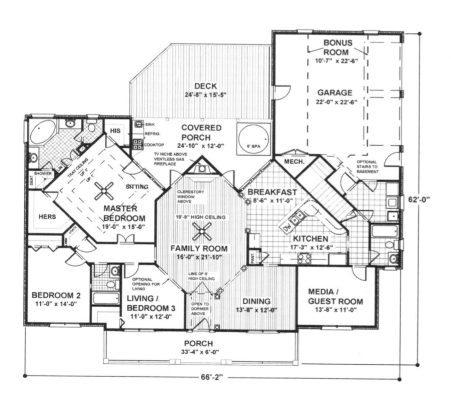

Triple Dormers Create Terrific Curb Appeal

Special features

- 1,992 total square feet of living area

- Interesting angled walls add drama to many of the living areas including family room, master bedroom and breakfast area

- Covered porch includes spa and an outdoor kitchen with sink, refridgerator and cooktop

- Enter majestic master bath to find a dramatic corner oversized tub

- 4 bedrooms, 3 baths, 2-car side entry garage

- Basement, crawl space or slab foundation, please specify when ordering

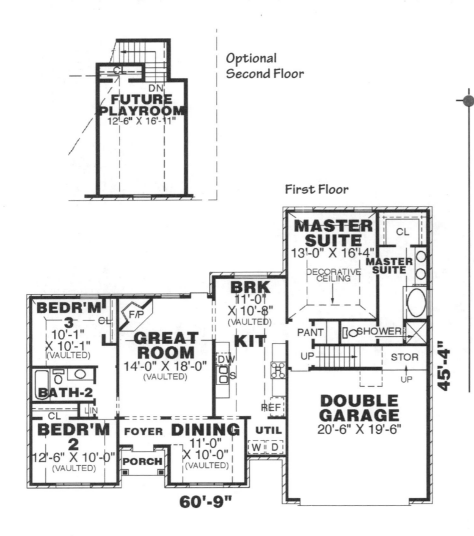

Optional
Second Floor

FUTURE PLAYROOM
12'-6" X 16'-11"

CL
DN

First Floor

MASTER SUITE
13'-0" X 16'-4"

CL

MASTER SUITE

DECORATIVE CEILING

BRK
11'-0"
X 10'-8"
(VAULTED)

BEDR'M 3
10'-1"
X 10'-1"
(VAULTED)

F/P

GREAT ROOM
14'-0" X 18'-0"
(VAULTED)

KIT

PANT

SHOWER

UP

STOR

UP

DW

BATH-2

CL   LIN

REF

DOUBLE GARAGE
20'-6" X 19'-6"

BEDR'M 2
12'-6" X 10'-0"
(VAULTED)

FOYER

DINING
11'-0"
X 10'-0"
(VAULTED)

UTIL

W   D

PORCH

45'-4"

60'-9"

Vaulted Ceilings Throughout Home

Special features

- 1,634 total square feet of living area
- Enter foyer to find a nice-sized dining room to the right and a cozy great room with fireplace straight ahead
- Secluded master suite offers privacy from other bedrooms and living areas
- Plenty of storage throughout this home
- Bonus room on the second floor has an additional 256 square feet of living area
- 3 bedrooms, 2 baths, 2-car garage
- Slab foundation

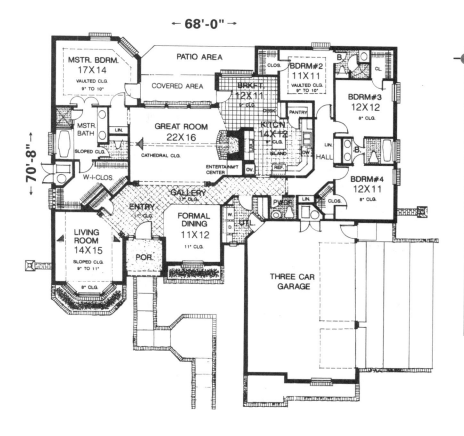

Fireplace Warms Large Great Room

Special features

- 2,578 total square feet of living area
- Enormous entry has an airy feel with gallery area nearby
- Living room with bay window is tucked away from traffic areas
- Large kitchen and breakfast area access covered patio
- Great room has entertainment center, fireplace and cathedral ceiling
- 4 bedrooms, 3 1/2 baths, 3-car side entry garage
- Slab foundation

Second Floor

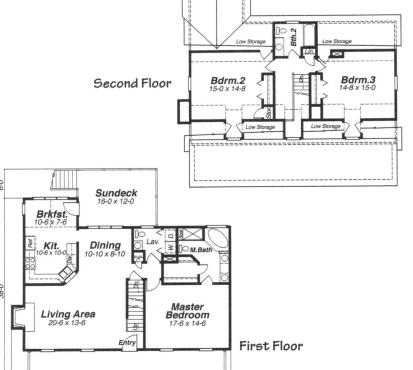

First Floor

Ideal For Entertaining

Special features

- 1,870 total square feet of living area
- Kitchen is open to the living and dining areas
- Breakfast area has cathedral ceiling creating a sunroom effect
- Master suite is spacious with all the amenities
- Second floor bedrooms share hall bath
- 3 bedrooms, 2 1/2 baths, 2-car drive under garage
- Basement foundation
- 1,159 square feet on the first floor and 711 square feet on the second floor

Plan #X26-LBD-26-23A

Price Code E

Floor plan labels:

- BEDRM 4 — 14-8 X 12-8 — 9 FT CLG
- COVERED PORCH — 9 FT CLG
- FAMILY ROOM — 13-6 X 16-6 — 9 FT CLG
- FP
- PORCH — 9 FT CLG
- HERS / HIS
- STEP MASTER BATH — 11 FT TRAY CLG
- SEAT
- MASTER BEDRM — 15-0 X 17-4 — 11 FT TRAY CLG
- BRKFST RM — 10-8 X 11-6 — 9 FT CLG
- BATH 2
- LIVING ROOM — 18-4 X 18-6 — 11 FT CLG
- KITCHEN — 13-6 X 11-4 — 9 FT CLG
- 42" LEDGE
- PWDR
- PAN
- UTIL — 12-6 X 5-8 — 9 FT CLG
- BEDRM 3 — 11-0 X 13-4 — 9 FT CLG
- BEDRM 2/ STUDY — 11-6 X 13-0 — 11 FT TRAY CLG
- FOYER — 11 FT CLG
- DINING ROOM — 14-0 X 13-6 — 11 FT CLG
- GARAGE
- PORCH — 9 FT CLG
- DEPTH 67-9
- WIDTH 70-2
- COPYRIGHT LARRY E. BELK

Step Up Into Master Bath Tub

Special features

- 2,678 total square feet of living area
- Elegant arched opening graces entrance
- Kitchen has double ovens, walk-in pantry and an eating bar
- Master bedroom has beautiful bath spotlighting step up tub
- 4 bedrooms, 2 1/2 baths, 2-car side entry garage
- Crawl space or slab foundation, please specify when ordering

Second Floor

TWO STORY GRAND ROOM

BRK. BELOW

BEDROOM 4
11'-11" x 13'-7"

BALCONY

B#3

TWO STORY FOYER

BEDROOM 3
11'-4" x 14'-6"

B#2

BEDROOM 2
12'-2" x 12'-0"

W.I.C.

W.I.C.

M.BATH

HERS

HIS

TWO STORY GRAND ROOM
17'-3" x 19'-5"

BREAKFAST

KITCHEN

MASTER BEDROOM
14'-6" x 17'-2"

TWO STORY FOYER
9'-11" x 11'-11"

DINING
12'-4" x 14'-7"

P.R.

PANTRY

LAUNDRY

LIVING/ OPT. SITTING
17'-9" x 14'-1"

TWO CAR GARAGE

First Floor

Width: 60'-0"
Depth: 52'-4"

Masterful Detailing
Special features

- 3,029 total square feet of living area
- Brick traditional has dramatic arched entry and window wall
- Grand room has 1 1/2 story detailed fireplace
- Vaulted master bath has his/hers separate vanities and walk-in closets
- 4 bedrooms, 3 1/2 baths, 2-car side entry garage
- Basement foundation
- 2,115 square feet on the first floor and 914 square feet on the second floor

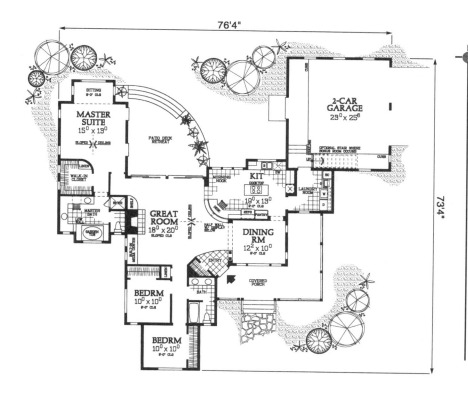

Wonderful, Compact Home

Special features

- 1,937 total square feet of living area

- Upscale great room offers a sloped ceiling, fireplace with extended hearth and built-in shelves for an entertainment center

- Gourmet kitchen includes a cooktop island counter and a quaint morning room

- Master suite features a sloped ceiling, cozy sitting room, walk-in closet and a private bath with whirlpool tub

- 3 bedrooms, 2 baths, 2-car side entry garage

- Crawl space foundation

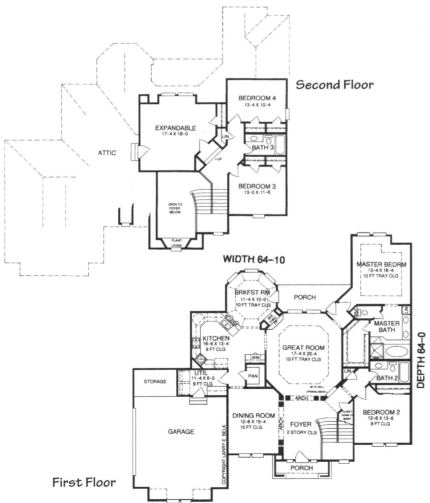

Second Floor

ATTIC

EXPANDABLE
17-4 X 18-0

BEDROOM 4
13-4 X 10-4

LIN

BATH 3

UP

BEDROOM 3
13-0 X 11-6

OPEN TO
FOYER
BELOW

PLANT
LEDGE

WIDTH 64-10

BRKFST RM
11-4 X 13-0
10 FT TRAY CLG

PORCH

MASTER BEDRM
13-4 X 16-4
10 FT TRAY CLG

KITCHEN
16-6 X 13-4
9 FT CLG

GREAT ROOM
17-4 X 20-4
10 FT TRAY CLG

MASTER
BATH

LIN

DESK

PAN

UTIL
11-4 X 6-0
9 FT CLG

STORAGE

BATH 2

36" HT WALL
OPENING ABOVE

ARCH

GARAGE

DINING ROOM
12-6 X 15-4
10 FT CLG

FOYER
2 STORY CLG

BEDROOM 2
12-6 X 13-6
9 FT CLG

COPYRIGHT LARRY E. BELK

ARCH

DEPTH 64-0

PORCH

First Floor

Stone And Brick, Elegant Facade

Special features

- 2,611 total square feet of living area

- Old world ambiance characterizes this European styled home

- Elegant stone entrance opens into two-story foyer

- Oversized great room features raised ceiling and see-through fireplace seen from the kitchen and breakfast room

- 4 bedrooms, 3 baths, 2-car side entry garage

- Basement, crawl space or slab foundation, please specify when ordering

- 2,050 square feet on the first floor and 561 square feet on the second floor

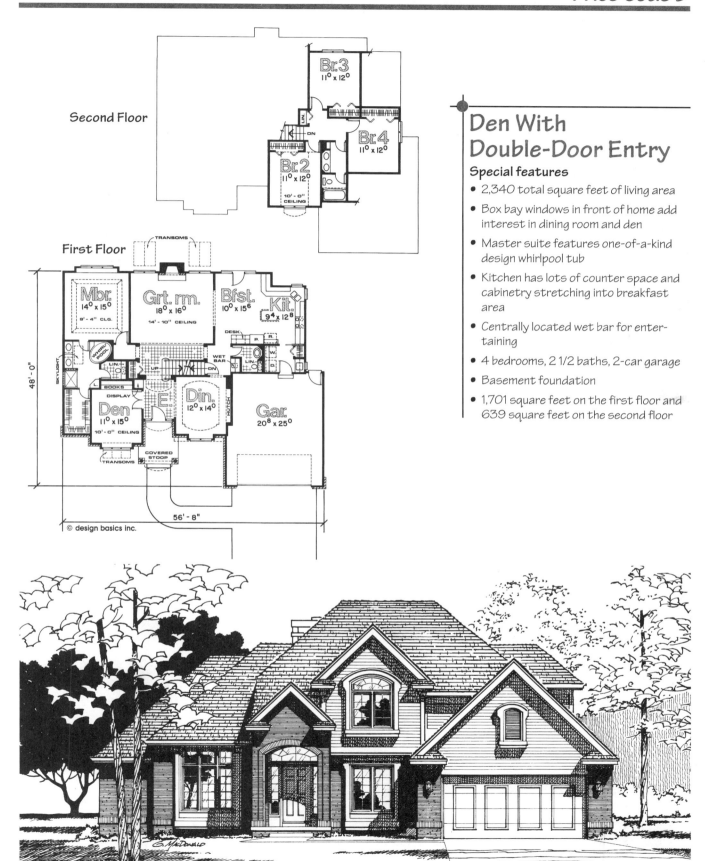

Second Floor

Br. 3
11⁰ x 12⁰

Br. 4
11⁰ x 12⁰

Br. 2
11⁰ x 12⁰
10' - 0" CEILING

First Floor

TRANSOMS

Mbr.
14⁰ x 15⁰
8' - 4" CLG.

Grt. rm.
18⁰ x 16⁰
14' - 10" CEILING

Bfst.
10⁰ x 15⁶

Kit.
9⁴ x 12⁸

WHIRL POOL

SKYLIGHT

LIN.

DESK

WET BAR

BOOKS

DISPLAY

Den
11⁰ x 15⁰
10' - 0" CEILING

Din.
12⁰ x 14⁰

HUTCH

Gar.
20⁸ x 25⁰

COVERED STOOP

TRANSOMS

48' - 0"

56' - 8"

© design basics inc.

Den With Double-Door Entry

Special features

- 2,340 total square feet of living area
- Box bay windows in front of home add interest in dining room and den
- Master suite features one-of-a-kind design whirlpool tub
- Kitchen has lots of counter space and cabinetry stretching into breakfast area
- Centrally located wet bar for entertaining
- 4 bedrooms, 2 1/2 baths, 2-car garage
- Basement foundation
- 1,701 square feet on the first floor and 639 square feet on the second floor

G. McDonald

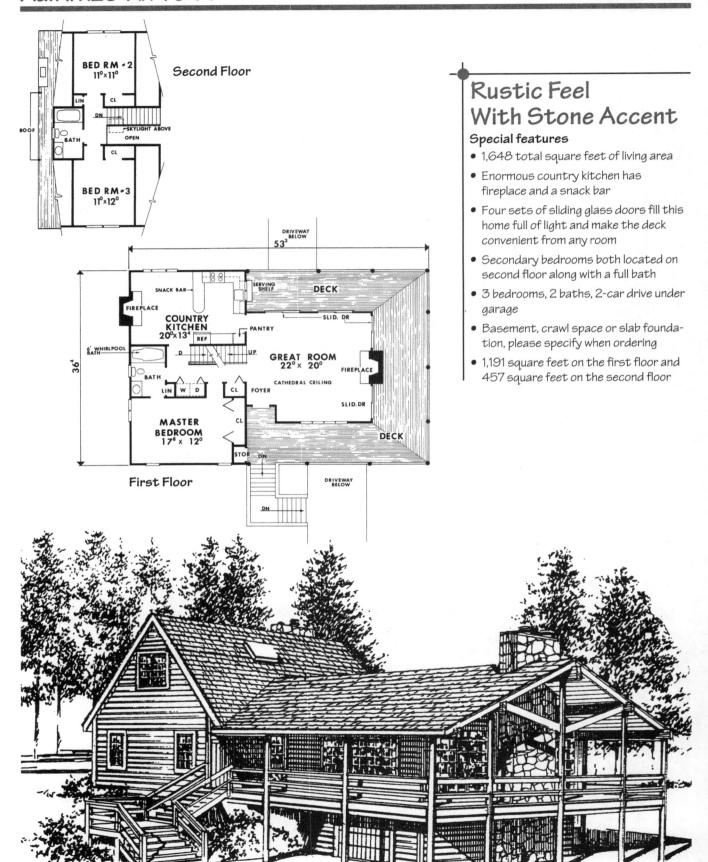

Rustic Feel With Stone Accent

Special features

- 1,648 total square feet of living area
- Enormous country kitchen has fireplace and a snack bar
- Four sets of sliding glass doors fill this home full of light and make the deck convenient from any room
- Secondary bedrooms both located on second floor along with a full bath
- 3 bedrooms, 2 baths, 2-car drive under garage
- Basement, crawl space or slab foundation, please specify when ordering
- 1,191 square feet on the first floor and 457 square feet on the second floor

Second Floor

First Floor

Plan #X26-SH-SEA-298

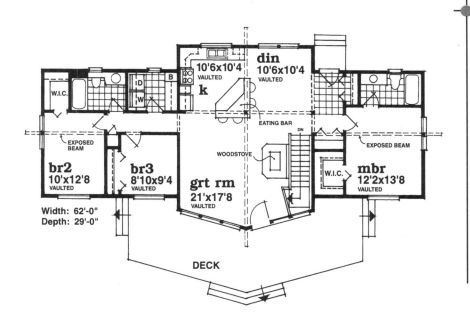

br2 10'x12'8 VAULTED

br3 8'10x9'4 VAULTED

grt rm 21'x17'8 VAULTED

mbr 12'2x13'8 VAULTED

din 10'6x10'4 VAULTED

k 10'6x10'4 VAULTED

W.I.C.

EXPOSED BEAM

WOODSTOVE

EATING BAR

EXPOSED BEAM

Width: 62'-0"
Depth: 29'-0"

DECK

Casual Living With This Family Design

Special features

- 1,405 total square feet of living area
- An expansive wall of glass gives a spectacular view to the great room and accentuates the high vaulted ceilings throughout the design
- Great room is warmed by a woodstove and is open to the dining room and L-shaped kitchen
- Triangular snack bar graces kitchen
- 3 bedrooms, 2 baths
- Basement or crawl space foundation, please specify when ordering

Irresistible Farmhouse

Special features

- 2,484 total square feet of living area
- Convenient first floor master suite features his and hers walk-in closets and a dramatic bath with whirlpool and separate vanities
- Living room has 18' ceiling with a radius top window, decorative columns and a plant shelf
- Family room includes built-in bookcases and double French doors leading to outdoor deck
- Bonus room has an additional 262 square feet of living area on the second floor
- 3 bedrooms, 2 1/2 baths, 2-car garage
- Basement or crawl space foundation, please specify when ordering
- 1,886 square feet on the first floor and 598 square feet on the second floor

Second Floor

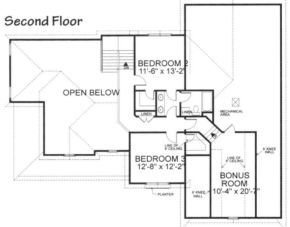

First Floor

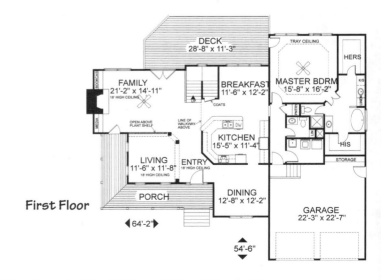

Width: 74'-0"
Depth: 65'-0"

© David C. Lutz

Sunny Sitting Area In Master Suite

Special features

- 2,545 total square feet of living area
- Beautiful covered front porch gives country appeal
- Open family room has 10' ceiling
- Kitchen has abundant counterspace
- 4 bedrooms, 2 1/2 baths, 3-car side entry garage
- Slab foundation

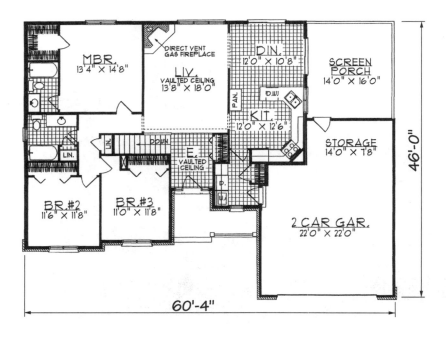

Terrific Ranch
Special features

- 1,540 total square feet of living area
- Spacious master bedroom has a large walk-in closet and sweeping windows overlooking yard
- First floor laundry conveniently located between the garage and kitchen
- Great room features a cathedral ceiling and corner fireplace
- 3 bedrooms, 2 baths, 2-car garage
- Basement foundation

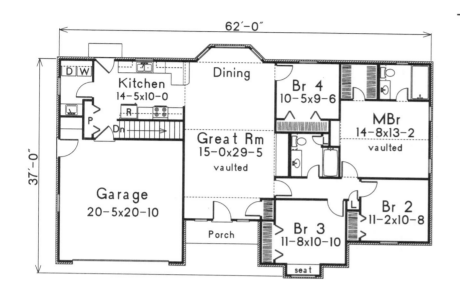

62'-0"

37'-0"

D | W
Kitchen
14-5x10-0
P
R
Dn

Dining

Br 4
10-5x9-6

MBr
14-8x13-2
vaulted

Great Rm
15-0x29-5
vaulted

Garage
20-5x20-10

Porch

Br 3
11-8x10-10

seat

Br 2
11-2x10-8

Colossal Great Room

Special features

- 1,599 total square feet of living area
- Efficiently designed kitchen with large pantry and easy access to laundry room
- Bedrooms #3 has charming window seat
- Master bedroom has a full bath and large walk-in closet
- 4 bedrooms, 2 baths, 2-car garage
- Basement foundation, drawings also include crawl space and slab foundations

Stone Accents

Special features

- 1,548 total square feet of living area
- 9' ceilings on the first floor
- Energy efficient home with 2" x 6" exterior walls
- Private study at the rear of the home makes an ideal office space with private entrance and half bath nearby
- 3 bedrooms, 2 1/2 baths, 1-car rear entry garage
- Crawl space foundation
- 761 square feet on the first floor and 787 square feet on the second floor

First Floor

24'

48'

STUDY
11/0 X 12/0

GARAGE
11/6 X 22/6

LIN.

REF

DINING
11/6 X 11/4

VAULTED
GREAT RM.
12/0 X 13/4

UP

©Alan Mascord Design Associates, Inc.

Second Floor

VAULTED
MASTER
11/0 X 15/0

BR. 2
11/8 X 13/0

DN.

BR. 3
11/0 X 11/0

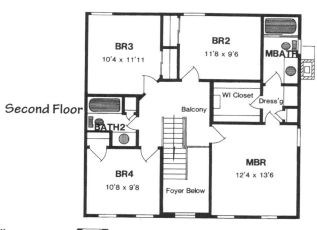

Second Floor

BR3
10'4 x 11'11

BR2
11'8 x 9'6

MBATH

WI Closet

Dress'g

Balcony

BATH2

BR4
10'8 x 9'8

Foyer Below

MBR
12'4 x 13'6

Width: 52'-8"
Depth: 41'-8"

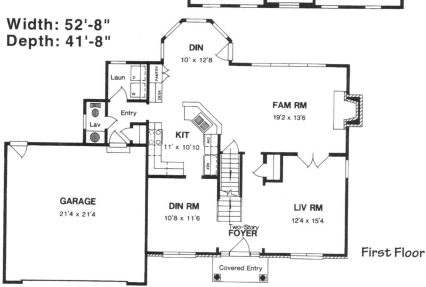

DIN
10' x 12'8

Laun

PANTRY

DESK

Entry

Lav

FAM RM
19'2 x 13'6

KIT
11' x 10'10

REF

GARAGE
21'4 x 21'4

DIN RM
10'8 x 11'6

Two-Story
FOYER

LIV RM
12'4 x 15'4

First Floor

Covered Entry

Classic Features

Special features

- 1,992 total square feet of living area
- Sunny family room has lots of windows and a large fireplace
- Octagon-shaped dining area is adjacent to kitchen for easy access
- Formal living room is separated from family room by double-doors
- Master bedroom has private bath with dressing area and walk-in closet
- 4 bedrooms, 2 1/2 baths, 2-car garage
- Basement foundation
- 1,100 square feet on the first floor and 892 square feet on the second floor

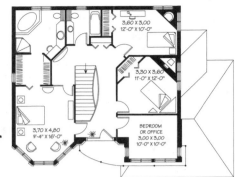

Second Floor

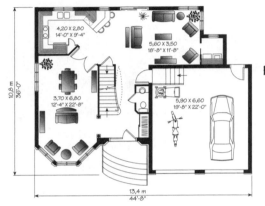

First Floor

European Styling With A Contemporary Feel

Special features

- 1,976 total square feet of living area
- 9' ceiling on first floor
- French doors between dining and family rooms
- Energy efficient home with 2" x 6" exterior walls
- 3 bedrooms, 2 1/2 baths, 2-car garage
- Basement foundation
- 924 square feet on the first floor and 1,052 square feet on the second floor

Second Floor

STORAGE

BEDROOM 3
15X12

DN
OPEN TO BELOW

BEDROOM 2
15X12

DECK

SKYLIGHT

DINING
12x12

KITCHEN
10x12

DN

VAULT

34

MASTER BEDRM
15x13

UP

VAULT

FAMILY ROOM
18x15

COATS

D

W

First Floor

38

Appealing Charming Porch

Special features

- 1,643 total square feet of living area

- First floor master bedroom has private bath, walk-in closet and easy access to laundry closet

- Comfortable family room features a vaulted ceiling and a cozy fireplace

- Two bedrooms on the second floor share a bath

- 3 bedrooms, 2 1/2 baths, 2-car drive under garage

- Basement or crawl space foundation, please specify when ordering

- 1,064 square feet on the first floor and 579 square feet on the second floor

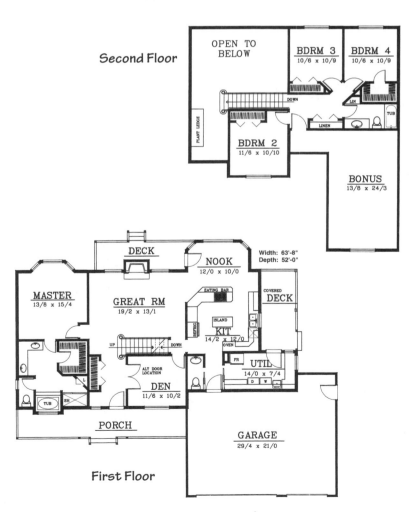

Second Floor

OPEN TO BELOW

BDRM 3
10/6 x 10/9

BDRM 4
10/6 x 10/9

PLANT LEDGE

DOWN

LINEN

TUB

BDRM 2
11/6 x 10/10

BONUS
13/8 x 24/3

First Floor

DECK

NOOK
12/0 x 10/0

Width: 63'-8"
Depth: 52'-0"

MASTER
13/8 x 15/4

GREAT RM
19/2 x 13/1

EATING BAR

COVERED
DECK

REFRIG

ISLAND

KIT
14/2 x 12/0

OVEN

UP

DOWN

ALT DOOR
LOCATION

FR

UTIL
14/0 x 7/4

D   W

DEN
11/6 x 10/2

TUB   SH

PORCH

GARAGE
29/4 x 21/0

Convenient First Floor Master Suite

Special features

- 2,504 total square feet of living area
- Efficient kitchen boasts a peninsula counter adding workspace as well as an eating bar
- The nook and kitchen blend nicely into the great room for family gathering
- The utility room has a soaking sink, extra counterspace and plenty of room for an additional refrigerator
- 4 bedrooms, 2 1/2 baths, 3-car garage
- Basement foundation
- 1,468 square feet on the first floor and 1,036 square feet on the second floor

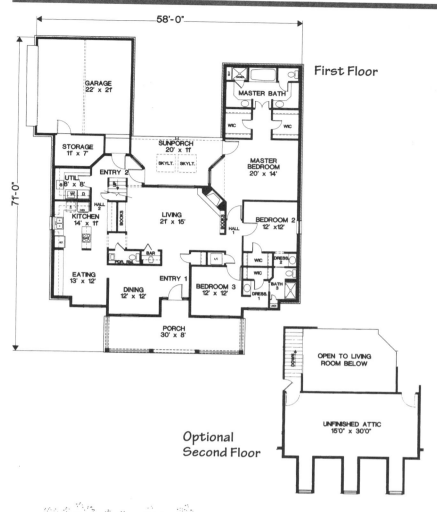

First Floor

GARAGE
22' x 21'

MASTER BATH

WIC   WIC

STORAGE
11' x 7'

SUNPORCH
20' x 11'

SKYLT.   SKYLT.

MASTER
BEDROOM
20' x 14'

ENTRY 2

UTIL
8' x 8'

HALL 2

KITCHEN
14' x 11'

BOOKS

LIVING
21' x 15'

BOOKS

HALL 1

BEDROOM 2
12' x12'

58'-0"

71'-0"

EATING
13' x 12'

POR. RM.   BAR

WIC
WIC

DRESS 2

ENTRY 1

DINING
12' x 12'

BEDROOM 3
12' x 12'

DRESS 1

BATH 3

PORCH
30' x 8'

**Optional
Second Floor**

OPEN TO LIVING
ROOM BELOW

DOWN

UNFINISHED ATTIC
15'0" x 30'0"

Expansive Counterspace

Special features

- 2,123 total square feet of living area
- Energy efficient home with 2" x 6" exterior walls
- Living room has wood burning fireplace, built-in bookshelves and a wet bar
- Skylights make sunporch bright and comfortable
- Unfinished attic has an additional 450 square feet of living area
- 3 bedrooms, 2 1/2 baths, 2-car side entry garage
- Crawl space, slab or basement foundation, please specify when ordering

Second Floor

BONUS RM.
17/0 X 14/8

FAMILY RM
BELOW

BR. 2
12/2 X 11/0

BR. 3
10/0 X 15/6

First Floor

59'

53'

MASTER
12/0 X 16/0

TWO STORY
FAMILY
13/8 X 18/0

NOOK
12/0 X 12/0

12/0 X 11/6

GARAGE
19/4 X 21/4

10/0 X 19/4

DINING
12/0 X 10/0

DEN
10/0 X 11/6

LIVING
12/0 X 14/6

PORCH

Combined Living

Special features

- 2,391 total square feet of living area
- Family room with fireplace and beautiful windows
- Formal living and dining areas in the front of the home have fireplace
- Master bedroom conveniently located on first floor
- Bonus room has an additional 417 square feet of living area
- 3 bedrooms, 2 1/2 baths, 3-car garage
- Crawl space foundation
- 1,811 square feet on the first floor and 580 square feet on the second floor

COPYRIGHTED 1997
G. MARQUIS

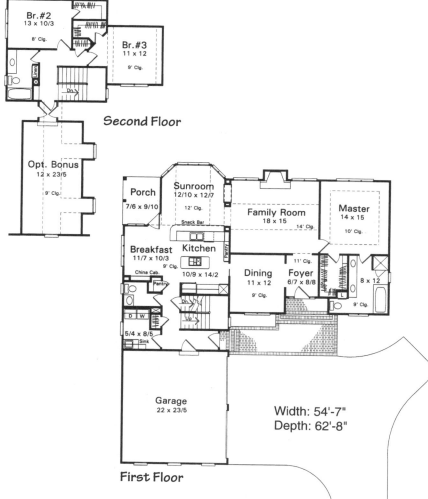

Second Floor

Br. #2
13 x 10/3
8' Clg.

Br. #3
11 x 12
9' Clg.

Linen

Dn.

Opt. Bonus
12 x 23/5
9' Clg.

First Floor

Porch
7/6 x 9/10

Sunroom
12/10 x 12/7
12' Clg.

Snack Bar

Family Room
18 x 15
14' Clg.

Master
14 x 15
10' Clg.

Breakfast
11/7 x 10/3

Kitchen
10/9 x 14/2
9' Clg.

Pantry

China Cab.

Pantry

Dining
11 x 12
9' Clg.

Foyer
6/7 x 8/8

11' Clg.

8 x 12

9' Clg.

Dn.

Up

D W

5/4 x 8/5

Sink

L

Garage
22 x 23/5

Width: 54'-7"
Depth: 62'-8"

Bay Creates
Bright Sunroom

Special features

- 2,148 total square feet of living area
- Cheerful bayed sunroom has attached porch and overlooks kitchen and breakfast area
- Varied ceiling heights throughout entire plan
- All bedrooms have walk-in closets
- Laundry area includes handy sink
- 3 bedrooms, 2 1/2 baths, 2-car side entry garage
- Basement foundation
- 1,626 square feet on the first floor and 522 square feet on the second floor

Stucco Adds Excitement To This Traditional Ranch

Special features

- 2,350 total square feet of living area
- Luxurious master suite with large bath and enormous walk-in closet
- Built-in hutch in breakfast room is eye-catching
- Terrific study located in its own private hall with half bath includes two closets and a bookcase
- 3 bedrooms, 2 1/2 baths, 2-car side entry garage
- Walk-out basement, crawl space or slab foundation, please specify when ordering

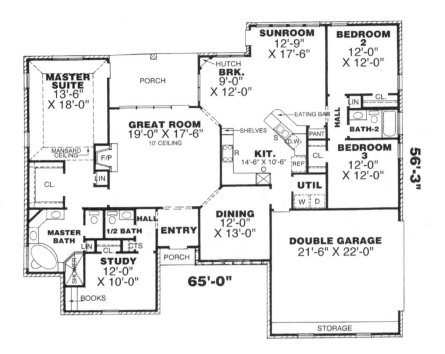

Second Floor

First Floor

Inviting Oversized Porch

Special features

- 2,135 total square feet of living area
- All bedrooms on second floor for privacy
- 9' ceilings on first floor
- Energy efficient home has 2" x 6" exterior walls
- 4 bedrooms, 2 1/2 baths, 2-car side entry garage
- Basement foundation
- 1,050 square feet on the first floor and 1,085 square feet on the second floor

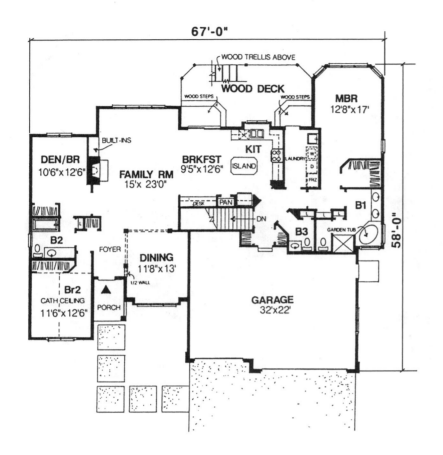

67'-0"

WOOD TRELLIS ABOVE

WOOD DECK

WOOD STEPS   WOOD STEPS

MBR
12'8"x 17'

BUILT-INS

DEN/BR
10'6"x 12'6"

FAMILY RM
15'x 23'0"

BRKFST
9'5"x 12'6"

KIT
ISLAND

LAUNDRY

W
D
FRZ

B1

B2

FOYER

DESK PAN

DN

B3

GARDEN TUB

DINING
11'8"x 13'

1/2 WALL

Br2
CATH CEILING
11'6"x 12'6"

PORCH

GARAGE
32'x22'

58'-0"

Spacious Ranch Style
Special features

- 2,086 total square feet of living area
- Corner garden tub graces private master bath
- Kitchen and breakfast room have terrific placement connecting to family room which creates a feeling of openness
- Secluded den makes an ideal office space
- 9' ceilings throughout this home
- 3 bedrooms, 2 1/2 baths, 3-car garage
- Basement foundation

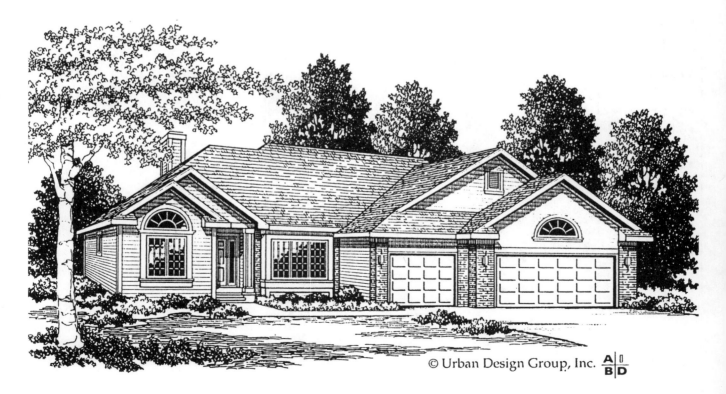

© Urban Design Group, Inc.

A 0
B D

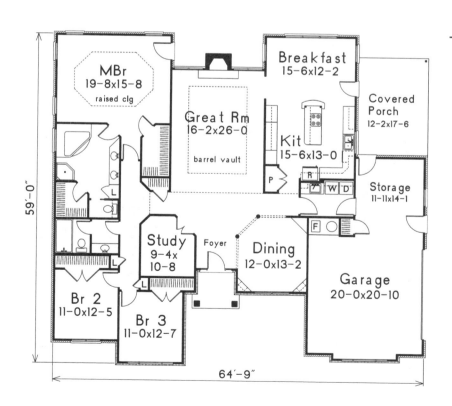

Well-Designed Floor Plan Has Many Extras

Special features

- 2,437 total square feet of living area
- Spacious breakfast area with access to the covered porch is adjacent to kitchen and great room
- Elegant dining area has columned entrance and built-in corner cabinets
- Cozy study has handsome double-door entrance off a large foyer
- Raised ceiling and lots of windows in master suite create a spacious, open feel
- 3 bedrooms, 2 baths, 2-car side entry garage
- Slab foundation, drawings also include crawl space foundation

Unique Angled Entry

Special features

- 1,150 total square feet of living area
- Master suite has its own private sitting area
- Living and dining rooms have 11' high box ceiling
- Ornate trim work accents the wood sided exterior
- 2 bedrooms, 2 baths, 2-car garage
- Slab or crawl space foundation, please specify when ordering

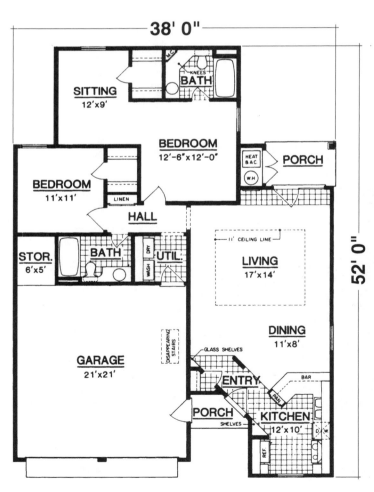

Secluded Master Suite

Special features

- 1,819 total square feet of living area
- Master suite features access to the outdoors, large walk-in closet and private bath
- 9' ceilings throughout
- Formal foyer with coat closet opens into vaulted great room with fireplace and formal dining room
- Kitchen and breakfast room create cozy casual area
- 3 bedrooms, 2 baths, 2-car side entry garage
- Basement foundation

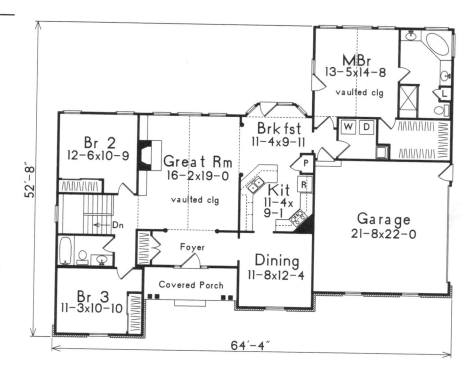

© Michael E. Nelson
NELSON DESIGN GROUP, LLC

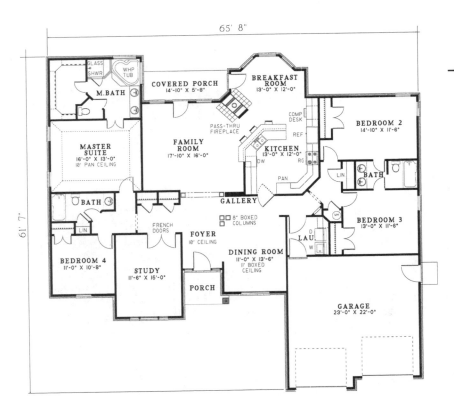

Varied Ceiling Heights

Special features

- 2,439 total square feet of living area
- Enter columned gallery area just before reaching family room with see-through fireplace
- Master suite has a corner whirlpool tub
- Double-door entrance into study
- 4 bedrooms, 3 baths, 2-car garage
- Slab, crawl space, basement or walk-out basement foundation, please specify when ordering

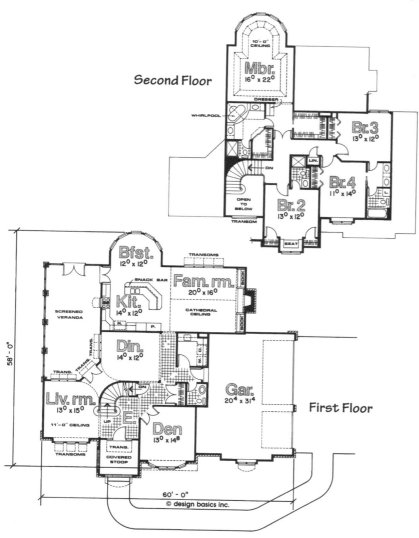

Second Floor

First Floor

Elaborate Master Suite

Special features

- 3,057 total square feet of living area
- Oversized rooms throughout
- Peaceful second floor master suite with dramatic bay window
- Living and dining rooms connect to screened veranda through beautiful double-doors
- 4 bedrooms, 3 1/2 baths, 3-car side entry garage
- Basement foundation
- 1,631 square feet on the first floor and 1,426 square feet on the second floor

Corner Fireplace In Great Room

Special features

- 1,642 total square feet of living area
- Built-in cabinet in dining room adds a custom feel
- Secondary bedrooms share an oversized bath
- Master bedroom includes private bath with dressing table
- 3 bedrooms, 2 baths, 2-car garage
- Crawl space foundation

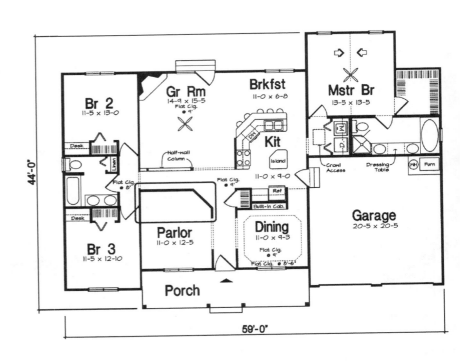

Kitchen With Island Sink

Special features

- 2,010 total square feet of living area
- Oversized kitchen is a great gathering place with eat-in island bar, dining area nearby and built-in desk
- First floor master bedroom has privacy
- Unique second floor kid's living area for playroom
- 3 bedrooms, 2 1/2 baths, 2-car side entry garage
- Basement foundation
- 1,269 square feet on the first floor and 741 square feet on the second floor

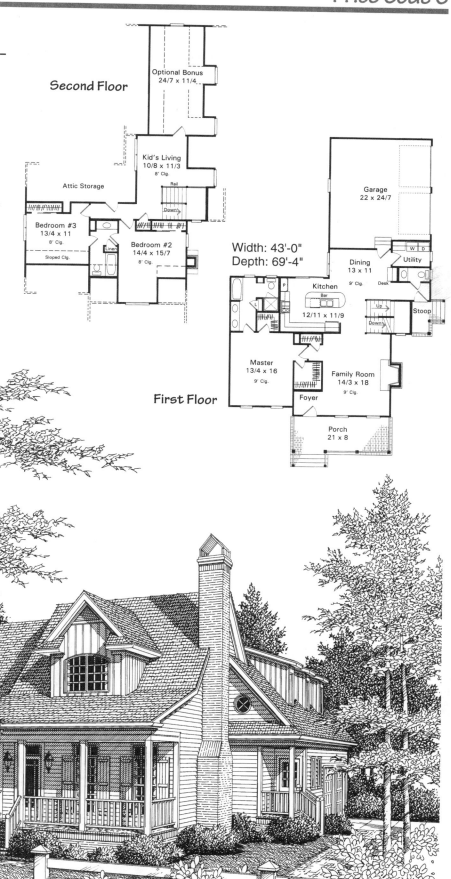

Second Floor

Optional Bonus
24/7 x 11/4

Kid's Living
10/8 x 11/3
8' Clg.

Attic Storage

Rail

Down

Bedroom #3
13/4 x 11
8' Clg.

Linen

Bedroom #2
14/4 x 15/7
8' Clg.

Sloped Clg.

Garage
22 x 24/7

Width: 43'-0"
Depth: 69'-4"

Dining
13 x 11
9' Clg.

Utility

W D

P

Kitchen
Bar
12/11 x 11/9

Desk

Up

Down

Stoop

Master
13/4 x 16
9' Clg.

Family Room
14/3 x 18
9' Clg.

Foyer

First Floor

Porch
21 x 8

© Michael E. Nelson
NELSON DESIGN GROUP, LLC

Cozy
Covered Porches

Special features

- 2,502 total square feet of living area

- Great room has fireplace, a media center and built-in bookshelves

- Kitchen has counter and table seating in breakfast area

- Laundry area with extra storage

- Optional golf cart storage area in garage

- 4 bedrooms, 2 baths, 2-car side entry garage

- Walk-out basement, basement, crawl space or slab foundation, please specify when ordering

Second Floor

First Floor

Appealing Master Suite

Special features

- 1,896 total square feet of living area
- Living room has lots of windows, a media center and a fireplace
- Centrally located kitchen with breakfast nook
- Extra storage in garage
- Covered porched in front and rear of home
- Optional balcony on second floor
- 4 bedrooms, 2 1/2 baths, 2-car garage
- Basement, crawl space or slab foundation, please specify when ordering
- 1,235 square feet on the first floor and 661 square feet on the second floor

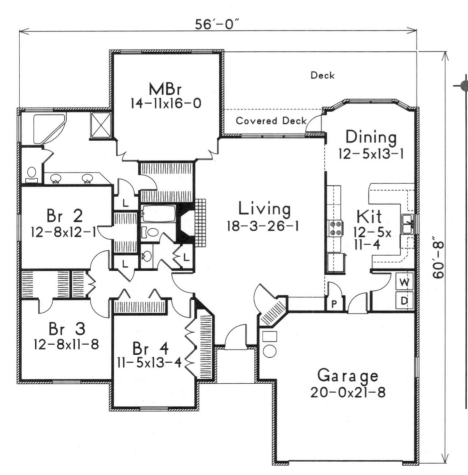

Inviting
Gabled Entry

Special features

- 2,128 total square feet of living area

- Versatile kitchen has plenty of space for entertaining with large dining area and counter seating

- Luxurious master bedroom has double-door entry and private bath with jacuzzi tub, double sinks and large walk-in closet

- Secondary bedrooms include spacious walk-in closets

- Coat closet in front entry is a nice added feature

- 4 bedrooms, 2 baths, 2-car garage

- Slab foundation, drawings also include crawl space foundation

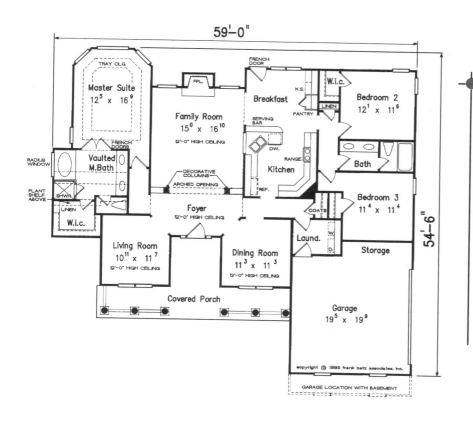

Impressive Foyer

Special features

- 1,856 total square feet of living area
- Beautiful covered porch creates a Southern accent
- Kitchen has an organized feel with lots of cabinetry
- Large foyer has a grand entrance and leads into family room through columns and arched opening
- 3 bedrooms, 2 baths, 2-car side entry garage
- Walk-out basement, crawl space or slab foundation, please specify when ordering

Award Winning Style With This Design

Special features

- 2,156 total square feet of living area
- Secluded master bedroom has spa style bath with corner whirlpool tub, large shower double sinks and walk-in closet
- Kitchen overlooks rear patio
- Plenty of windows add an open, airy feel to the great room
- 3 bedrooms, 3 baths, 2-car side entry garage
- Basement, crawl space or slab foundation, please specify when ordering

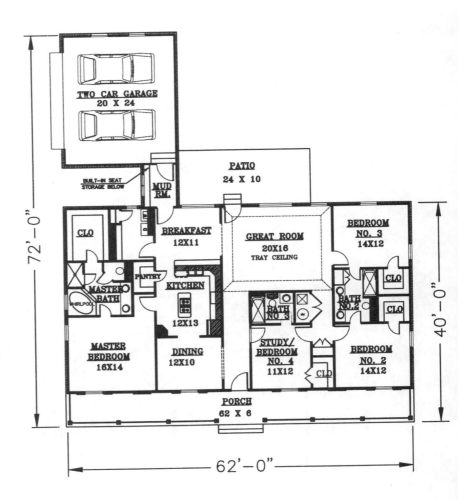

TO ORDER SEE PAGE 320 OR CALL TOLL-FREE 1-800-DREAM HOME (373-2646)

Second Floor

BEDROOM 3
10'-8" X 11'-9"

M. BATH
13'-10" X 12'-6"

WHP TUB

10'-8" X 6'-6"

BEDROOM 2
14'-2" X 11'-9"

MASTER SUITE
16'-8" X 17'-0"
10' BOXED CEILING

LIN

BALCONY

COVERED PORCH
6'-6" X 46'-8"

Columned Facade

Special features

- 2,247 total square feet of living area
- Enormous great room with fireplace extends into a kitchen with center island
- Formal dining area is quiet, yet convenient to kitchen
- All bedrooms located on second floor maintain privacy
- 3 bedrooms, 2 1/2 baths, 2-car side entry garage
- Basement, crawl space or slab foundation, please specify when ordering
- 1,154 square feet on the first floor and 1,093 square feet on the second floor

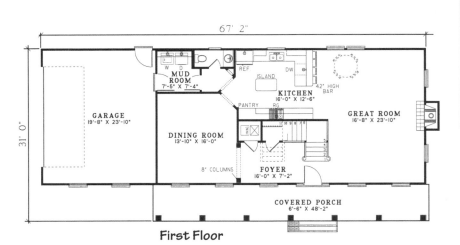

67' 2"

31' 0"

GARAGE
19'-8" X 23'-10"

MUD ROOM
7'-5" X 7'-4"

W D

REF DW

ISLAND

KITCHEN
16'-0" X 12'-6"

42" HIGH BAR

PANTRY

DINING ROOM
13'-10" X 16'-0"

GREAT ROOM
16'-8" X 23'-10"

RG

8" COLUMNS

FOYER
16'-0" X 7'-2"

COVERED PORCH
6'-6" X 48'-2"

First Floor

HOLZHAUER 96

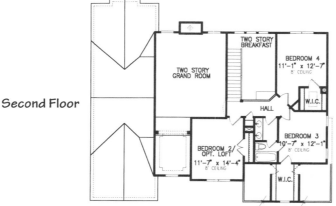

Second Floor

TWO STORY GRAND ROOM

TWO STORY BREAKFAST

BEDROOM 4
11'-1" x 12'-7"
8' CEILING

HALL

W.I.C.

BEDROOM 2/
OPT. LOFT
11'-7" x 14'-4"
8' CEILING

BEDROOM 3
10'-7" x 12'-1"
8' CEILING

W.I.C.

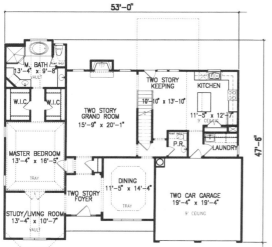

53'-0"

M. BATH
13'-4" x 9'-8"
VAULT

W.I.C. W.I.C.

TWO STORY
GRAND ROOM
15'-9" x 20'-1"

TWO STORY
KEEPING
10'-10" x 13'-10"

KITCHEN
11'-5" x 12'-7"
9' CEILING

MASTER BEDROOM
13'-4" x 16'-5"
TRAY

P.R.

LAUNDRY

47'-6"

TWO STORY
FOYER

DINING
11'-5" x 14'-4"
TRAY

TWO CAR GARAGE
19'-4" x 19'-4"
9' CEILING

STUDY/LIVING ROOM
13'-4" x 10'-7"
VAULT

First Floor

Windows Add Plenty Of Light

Special features

- 2,450 total square feet of living area
- Convenient first floor master bedroom has double walk-in closets and an optional sitting area/study
- Two-story breakfast and grand room are open and airy
- Laundry room has a sink and overhead cabinets for convenience
- 4 bedrooms, 2 1/2 baths, 2-car garage
- Basement or slab foundation, please specify when ordering
- 1,751 square feet on the first floor and 709 square feet on the second floor

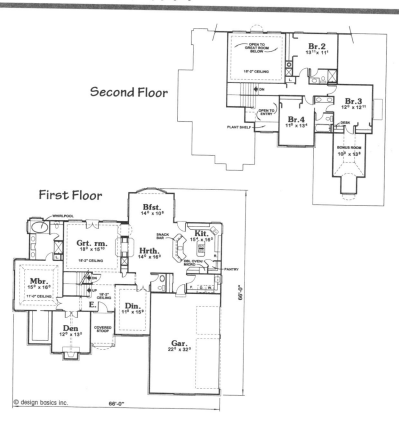

Second Floor

OPEN TO GREAT ROOM BELOW
18'-2" CEILING
DN
OPEN TO ENTRY
PLANT SHELF

Br. 2
13¹¹ x 11¹

Br. 3
12⁰ x 12¹¹

DESK

Br. 4
11⁰ x 13⁴

BONUS ROOM
10⁵ x 13⁸

First Floor

WHIRLPOOL

Grt. rm.
18⁰ x 15¹⁰
18'-2" CEILING

SNACK BAR

Hrth.
14⁰ x 16⁰

Kit.
15⁴ x 16⁰

DBL OVEN/ MICRO

PANTRY

Mbr.
15⁰ x 16⁰
11'-0" CEILING

DN
UP
18'-2" CEILING

E.

Den
12⁰ x 13⁰

COVERED STOOP

Din.
11⁰ x 15⁹

Bfst.
14⁰ x 10⁸

F. D. W.

Gar.
22⁰ x 32⁰

66'-0"

66'-0"

© design basics inc.

Two-Story Great Room

Special features

- 3,040 total square feet of living area
- Cozy hearth room is the heart of the design with see-through fireplace connecting it to the two-story great room
- Den has a fireplace
- Large master suite with oversized walk-in closet
- Possible expansion with bonus room on second floor
- 4 bedrooms, 3 1/2 baths, 3-car side entry garage
- Basement foundation
- 2,215 square feet on the first floor and 825 square feet on the second floor

DESIGNERS' INK

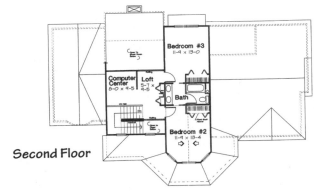

Second Floor

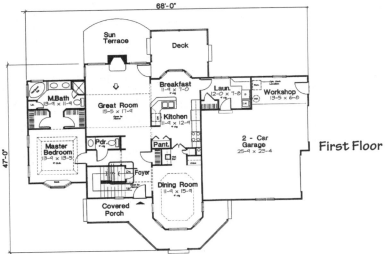

First Floor

Unique Octagon-Shaped Porch

Special features

- 2,044 total square feet of living area
- Formal dining area easily accesses kitchen through double-doors
- Two-car garage features a workshop area for projects or extra storage
- Second floor includes loft space ideal for office area and a handy computer center
- Colossal master bedroom with double walk-in closets, private bath bay window seat
- 3 bedrooms, 2 1/2 baths, 2-car side entry garage
- Basement, crawl space or slab foundation, please specify when ordering
- 1,403 square feet on the first floor and 641 square feet on the second floor

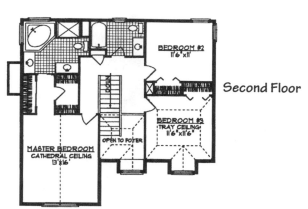

Second Floor

BEDROOM #2
11'6"x11'

BEDROOM #3
TRAY CEILING
11'6"x11'6"

OPEN TO FOYER

MASTER BEDROOM
CATHEDRAL CEILING
13'x16'

First Floor

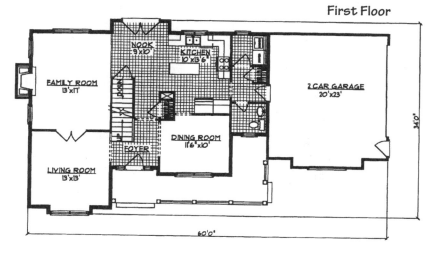

NOOK
9'x10'

KITCHEN
10'x13'6"

FAMILY ROOM
13'x17'

2 CAR GARAGE
20'x23'

DINING ROOM
11'6"x10'

FOYER

LIVING ROOM
13'x13'

34'0"

60'0"

Victorian Details Enhance This Home

Special features

- 1,986 total square feet of living area

- All bedrooms on second floor for privacy

- Open floor plan on first floor combines nook, family room and kitchen

- Formal living room in the front of the home is attached to the family room through double-doors

- Cathedral ceiling in master bedroom along with private bath and double closets makes a lovely space

- 3 bedrooms, 2 1/2 baths, 2-car side entry garage

- Basement foundation

- 1,065 square feet on the first floor and 921 square feet on the second floor

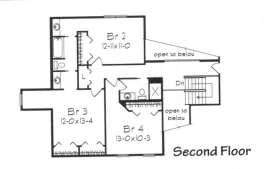

Second Floor

Outstanding Floor Plan For Year-Round Entertaining

Special features

- 2,597 total square feet of living area
- Large U-shaped kitchen features island cooktop and breakfast bar
- Entry and great room enhanced by sweeping balcony
- Bedrooms #2 and #3 share a bath, while the fourth bedroom has a private bath
- Vaulted great room with transomed arch windows
- 4 bedrooms, 3 1/2 baths, 2-car side entry garage
- Walk-out basement foundation, drawings also include crawl space and slab foundations
- 1,742 square feet on the first floor and 855 square feet on the second floor

First Floor

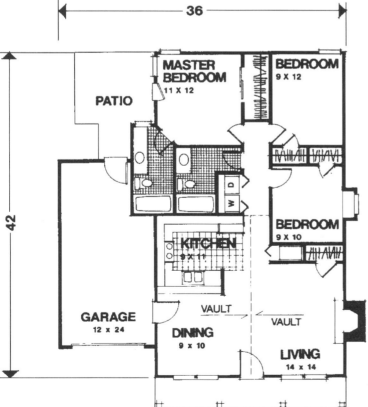

Open Living Spaces

Special features

- 1,050 total square feet of living area
- Master bedroom features a private bath and access outdoors onto a private patio
- A vaulted ceiling in the living and dining areas creates a feeling of spaciousness
- Laundry closet is convenient to all bedrooms
- Efficient U-shaped kitchen
- 3 bedrooms, 2 baths, 1-car garage
- Basement or slab foundation, please specify when ordering

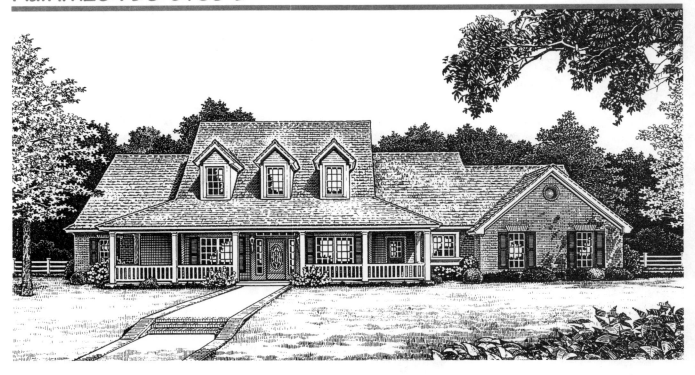

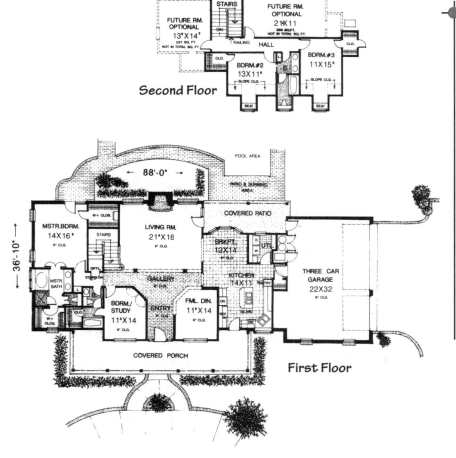

Second Floor

First Floor

Impressive Gallery

Special features

- 2,674 total square feet of living area

- First floor master bedroom has convenient location

- Kitchen and breakfast area have island and access to covered front porch

- Second floor bedrooms have dormer window seats for added charm

- Optional future room on second floor has an additional 520 square feet of living area

- 4 bedrooms, 3 baths, 3-car side entry garage

- Basement or slab foundation, please specify when ordering

- 2,074 square feet on the first floor and 600 square feet on the second floor

Plan #X26-BF-2108

Price Code C

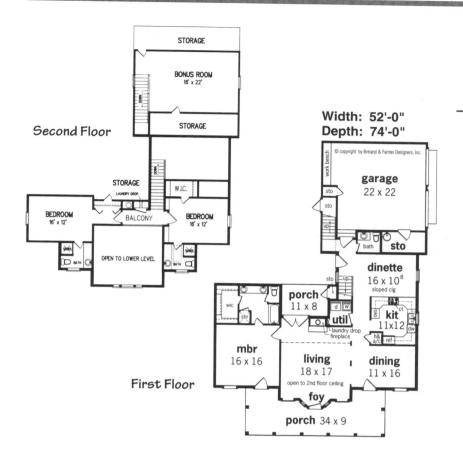

Second Floor

STORAGE

BONUS ROOM
16' x 22'

STORAGE

STORAGE

LAUNDRY DROP

W.I.C.

BEDROOM
16' x 12'

BALCONY

BEDROOM
16' x 12'

OPEN TO LOWER LEVEL

BATH

BATH

Width: 52'-0"
Depth: 74'-0"

© copyright by Breland & Farmer Designers, Inc.

work bench

garage
22 x 22

sto

sto

up

bath

sto

dinette
16 x 10⁸
sloped clg

sto   up

porch
11 x 8

d w

util
laundry drop
fireplace

kit
11x12

ovs

ct

dw

h&
a/c ref

wic

shr

mbr
16 x 16

First Floor

living
18 x 17
open to 2nd floor ceiling

dining
11 x 16

foy

porch 34 x 9

Two-Story Living Room

Special features

- 2,194 total square feet of living area
- Energy efficient home with 2" x 6" exterior walls
- Utility room has laundry drop conveniently located next to kitchen
- Both second floor bedrooms have large closets and their own bath
- 3 bedrooms, 3 1/2 baths, 2-car side entry garage
- Crawl space, slab or basement foundation, please specify when ordering
- 1,531 square feet on the first floor and 663 square feet on the second floor

Sophisticated Styling

Special features

- 1,595 total square feet of living area
- Vaulted master suite has sunny bay window
- Sliding glass doors in breakfast room lead to covered porch
- Extra storage in garage
- 3 bedrooms, 2 baths, 2-car side entry garage
- Basement, crawl space or slab foundation, please specify when ordering

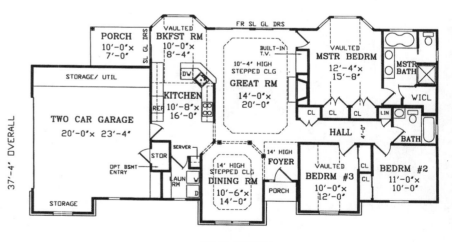

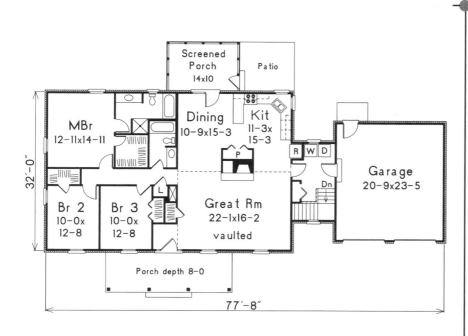

Sculptured Roof Line And Facade Add Charm

Special features

- 1,674 total square feet of living area
- Great room, dining area and kitchen, surrounded with vaulted ceiling, central fireplace and log bin
- Convenient laundry/mud room located between garage and family area with handy stairs to basement
- Easily expandable screened porch and adjacent patio with access from dining area
- Master bedroom features full bath with tub, separate shower and walk-in closet
- 3 bedrooms, 2 baths, 2-car garage
- Basement foundation, drawings also include crawl space and slab foundations

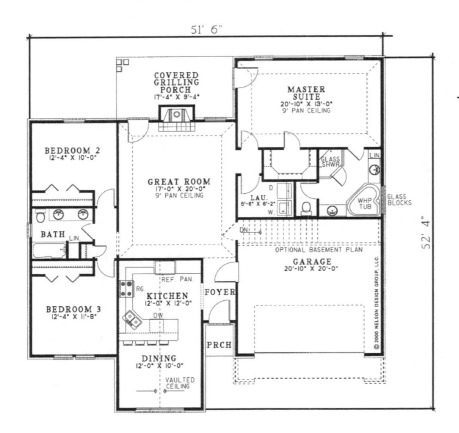

COVERED GRILLING PORCH
17'-4" X 9'-4"

MASTER SUITE
20'-10" X 13'-0"
9' PAN CEILING

BEDROOM 2
12'-4" X 10'-0"

GREAT ROOM
17'-0" X 20'-0"
9' PAN CEILING

GLASS SHWR.

LIN

D

LAU.
5'-6" X 6'-2"

WHP TUB

GLASS BLOCKS

BATH

LIN.

W

DN

OPTIONAL BASEMENT PLAN

GARAGE
20'-10" X 20'-0"

BEDROOM 3
12'-4" X 11'-8"

RG.
REF. PAN.
KITCHEN
12'-4" X 12'-0"
DW

FOYER

PRCH

DINING
12'-0" X 10'-0"

VAULTED CEILING

© 2000 NELSON DESIGN GROUP, LLC.

51' 6"

52' 4"

Master Suite Has Access Outdoors

Special features

- 1,680 total square feet of living area
- Enormous and luxurious master suite
- Kitchen and dining room have vaulted ceiling creating an open feeling
- Double sinks grace second bath
- 3 bedrooms, 2 baths, 2-car garage
- Walk-out basement or basement foundation, please specify when ordering

© Michael E. Nelson

Scalloped Front Porch

Special features

- 1,374 total square feet of living area
- Garage has extra storage space
- Spacious living room has fireplace
- Well-designed kitchen with adjacent breakfast nook
- Separated master suite maintains privacy
- 3 bedrooms, 2 baths, 2-car garage
- Slab or crawl space foundation, please specify when ordering

Sunny Eating Area

Special features

- 1,925 total square feet of living area

- Energy efficient design with 2" x 6" exterior walls

- Balcony off eating area adds character

- Master bedroom has a dressing room, large bath, walk-in closet and access to utility room

- 3 bedrooms, 2 baths, 2-car side entry garage

- Crawl space or slab foundation, please specify when ordering

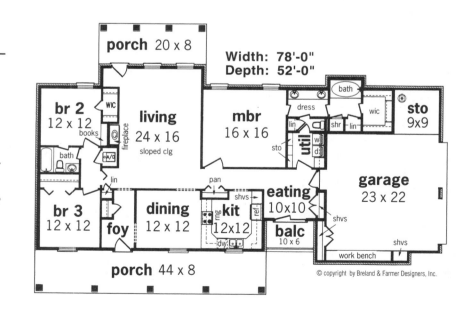

Width: 78'-0"
Depth: 52'-0"

porch 20 x 8

br 2 12 x 12
WIC
books
living 24 x 16 sloped clg
fireplace
bath
lin
br 3 12 x 12
foy
dining 12 x 12
pan
kit 12x12
eating 10x10
balc 10 x 6

mbr 16 x 16
dress
bath
wic
sto 9x9
lin
shr
lin
sto
util

garage 23 x 22
shvs
shvs
work bench

porch 44 x 8

© copyright by Breland & Farmer Designers, Inc.

Country Cottage

Special features

- 1,765 total square feet of living area
- Palladian window accenting stone gable adds new look to a popular cottage design
- Dormers open into vaulted area inside
- Kitchen extends to breakfast room with access to sun deck
- 3 bedrooms, 2 1/2 baths, 2-car drive under garage
- Basement foundation
- 1,210 square feet on the first floor and 555 square feet on the second floor

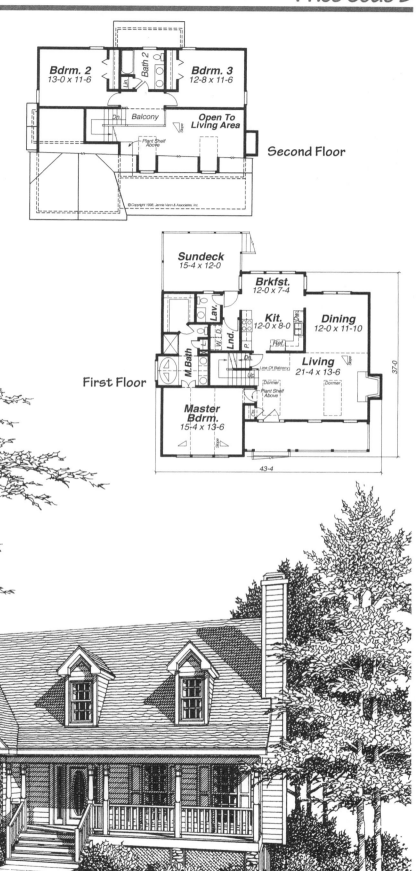

Second Floor

Bdrm. 2
13-0 x 11-6

Bath 2

Ln.

Bdrm. 3
12-8 x 11-6

Dn. Balcony

Open To Living Area

Plant Shelf Above

Slope

© Copyright 1996, Jannis Vann & Associates, Inc.

First Floor

Sundeck
15-4 x 12-0

Brkfst.
12-0 x 7-4

Kit.
12-0 x 8-0

Dining
12-0 x 11-10

Lav.

W.D.

Lnd.

P

Ref.

M.Bath

Dn.

Line Of Balcony

Up.

Living
21-4 x 13-6

Slope

Dormer

Plant Shelf Above

Dormer

Cls.

Master Bdrm.
15-4 x 13-6

Slope

37-0

43-4

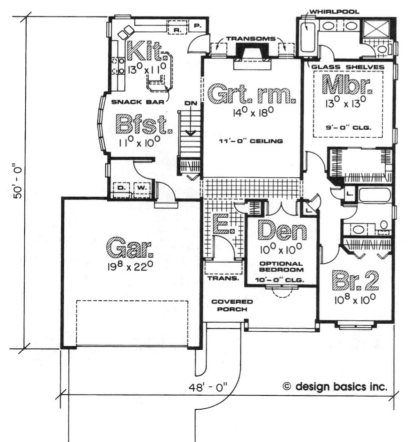

Great Design

Special features

- 1,479 total square feet of living area
- Centrally located great room enhanced with fireplace
- Den can easily convert to a third bedroom
- Master bedroom has private bath with large walk-in closet
- Sunny kitchen/breakfast room enjoys view into great room
- 2 bedrooms, 2 baths, 2-car garage
- Basement foundation

© design basics inc.

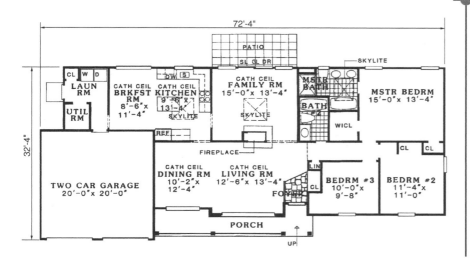

Attractive Gabled Roofline

Special features

- 1,615 total square feet of living area
- Master suite includes walk-in closet, spacious private bath with double vanity and a sloped ceiling with skylight
- Family room has space for built-ins adjacent to the fireplace
- Living and dining rooms are open to each other
- 3 bedrooms, 2 baths, 2-car garage
- Basement, slab or crawl space foundation, please specify when ordering

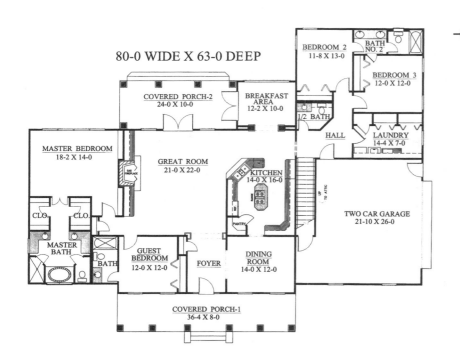

80-0 WIDE X 63-0 DEEP

BEDROOM 2
11-8 X 13-0

BATH NO. 2

BEDROOM 3
12-0 X 12-0

COVERED PORCH-2
24-0 X 10-0

BREAKFAST AREA
12-2 X 10-0

1/2 BATH

HALL

LAUNDRY
14-4 X 7-0

MASTER BEDROOM
18-2 X 14-0

GREAT ROOM
21-0 X 22-0

GAS FIREPLACE

KITCHEN
14-0 X 16-0

UP TO ATTIC

TWO CAR GARAGE
21-10 X 26-0

CLO.

CLO.

PANTRY

MASTER BATH

BATH

GUEST BEDROOM
12-0 X 12-0

FOYER

DINING ROOM
14-0 X 12-0

COVERED PORCH-1
36-4 X 8-0

Southern Elegance
Special features

- 2,669 total square feet of living area
- Nice-sized corner pantry in kitchen
- Guest bedroom or office located off the great room with a full bath
- Master bath has double walk-in closets, whirlpool bath and a large shower
- 3 bedrooms, 3 1/2 baths, 2-car side entry garage
- Basement or slab foundation, please specify when ordering

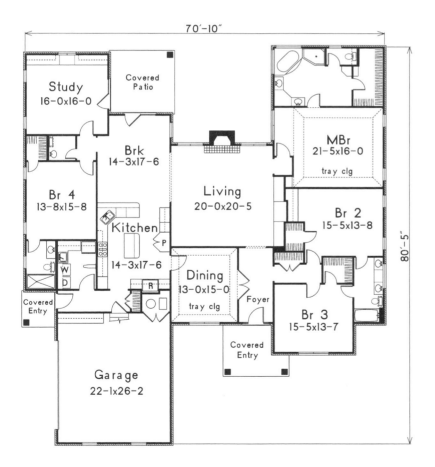

Study 16-0x16-0

Covered Patio

Brk 14-3x17-6

MBr 21-5x16-0 tray clg

Br 4 13-8x15-8

Living 20-0x20-5

Kitchen 14-3x17-6

Br 2 15-5x13-8

Dining 13-0x15-0 tray clg

Foyer

Covered Entry

Br 3 15-5x13-7

Covered Entry

Garage 22-1x26-2

70'-10"

80'-5"

Grand-Sized Living
Special features

- 3,366 total square feet of living area
- Wonderful covered patio off secluded study and breakfast area
- Separate dining area for entertaining
- Master suite has sitting area and private bath with exercise
- 4 bedrooms, 3 1/2 baths, 2-car side entry garage
- Crawl space or slab foundation, please specify when ordering

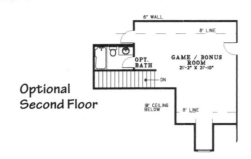

**Optional
Second Floor**

First Floor

Second Floor
Bonus Game Room
Special features

- 1,957 total square feet of living area
- Breakfast room with bay window opens to kitchen with bar
- 9' ceilings throughout this home
- Master suite has 10' boxed ceiling and atrium doors to rear porch
- 3 bedrooms, 2 baths, 2-car garage
- Basement, walk-out basement, slab or crawl space foundation, please specify when ordering

◄49'►

43'

VAULTED
DINING
11/0 X 14/0 +

VAULTED
LIVING
15/8 X 14/0

VAULTED
MASTER
13/0 X 11/8 +

8/0 X 12/8

PANTRY DESK   PLANT SHELF OVER AT 9'

GARAGE
19/4 X 19/8 +

LINEN

BR. 3
10/8 X 10/4

BR. 2
12/0 X 10/0

©Alan Mascord Design Associates, Inc.

Striking Plant Shelf

Special features

- 1,467 total square feet of living area
- Vaulted ceilings, an open floor plan and a wealth of windows create an inviting atmosphere
- Efficiently arranged kitchen has an island with built-in cooktop and a snack counter
- Plentiful storage and closet space throughout this home
- 3 bedrooms, 2 baths, 2-car garage
- Crawl space foundation

Classic Brick Ranch

Special features

- 2,097 total square feet of living area
- Angled kitchen, hearth room and eating areas add interest to this home
- Hearth room includes a TV niche making this a cozy place to relax
- Sumptuous master suite includes sitting area, his and hers walk-in closets and a full bath
- 3 bedrooms, 3 baths, 3-car side entry garage
- Crawl space or slab foundation, please specify when ordering

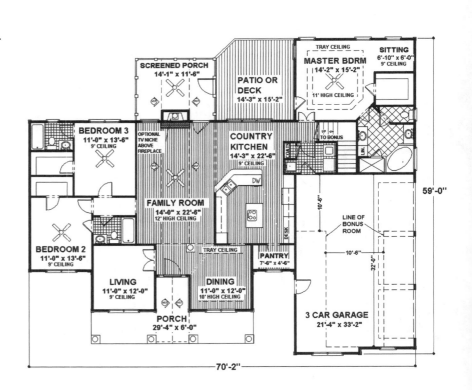

Luxurious Bay-Shaped Master Bath

Special features

- 2,962 total square feet of living area
- Vaulted breakfast nook adjacent to kitchen
- Bedroom #4 is an ideal guest suite with private bath
- Master suite includes see-through fireplace, bayed vanity and massive walk-in closet
- 4 bedrooms, 3 baths, 3-car side entry garage
- Slab foundation

Width: 66'-8"
Depth: 76'-8"

Home Designed For Outdoor Lifestyle

Special features

- 1,230 total square feet of living area
- Full-width deck creates plenty of outdoor living area
- The master bedroom accesses the deck through sliding glass doors and features a private bath
- Vaulted living room has a woodstove
- 3 bedrooms, 2 baths
- Crawl space or basement foundation, please specify when ordering

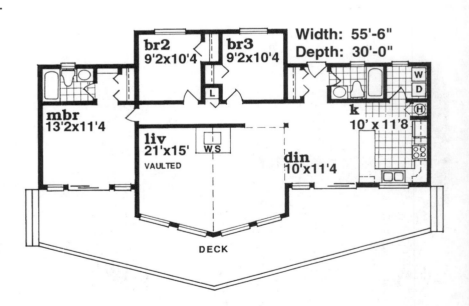

Width: 55'-6"
Depth: 30'-0"

br2 9'2x10'4
br3 9'2x10'4
L
mbr 13'2x11'4
liv 21'x15' VAULTED
W S
din 10'x11'4
k 10' x 11'8
W D H
DECK

Master Suite
With Sitting Area

Special features

- 2,188 total square feet of living area
- Master suite includes private covered porch
- Spacious kitchen has center island, snack bar and laundry access
- 3 bedrooms, 2 baths, 3-car side entry garage
- Basement foundation

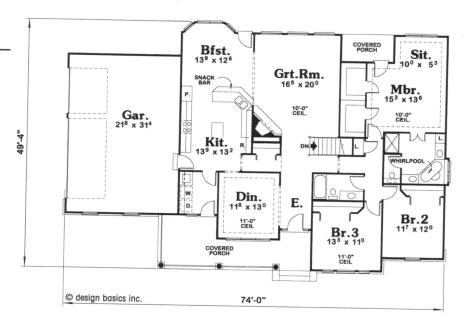

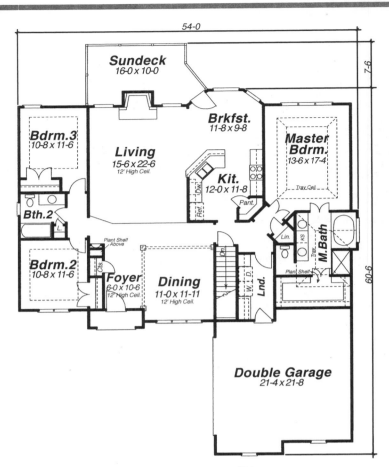

Sundeck
16-0 x 10-0

Brkfst.
11-8 x 9-8

Bdrm.3
10-8 x 11-6

Living
15-6 x 22-6
12' High Ceil.

Master
Bdrm.
13-6 x 17-4
Tray Ceil.

Kit.
12-0 x 11-8

Bth.2

M. Bath

Bdrm.2
10-8 x 11-6

Foyer
6-0 x 10-6
12' High Ceil.

Dining
11-0 x 11-11
12' High Ceil.

Plant Shelf
Above

Lnd.

Double Garage
21-4 x 21-8

54-0

7-6

60-6

Stone Accents
Inviting Entry

Special features

- 1,869 total square feet of living area
- Bayed breakfast area walks out to large sun deck
- Master bath has intricate ceiling design, double vanity, spa tub and a large walk-in closet
- Elegant columns frame formal dining area
- 3 bedrooms, 2 baths, 2-car side entry garage
- Basement, crawl space or slab foundation, please specify when ordering

KOIZUMI / BUTLER

Casual Country Home With Unique Loft

Special features

- 1,673 total square feet of living area
- Great room flows into the breakfast nook with outdoor access and beyond to an efficient kitchen
- Master suite on second floor has access to loft/study, private balcony and bath
- Covered porch surrounds the entire home for outdoor living area
- 3 bedrooms, 2 baths
- Crawl space foundation
- 1,093 square feet on the first floor and 580 square feet on the second floor

ATTIC ACCESS

BENCH

MASTER BATH

LOFT / STUDY
11¹⁰ x 7²

WALK-IN CLOSET

RAILING

OPEN TO BELOW

MASTER BEDRM
14⁶ x 15⁰

RAILING

BALCONY

RAILING

ATTIC ACCESS

SEAT

Second Floor

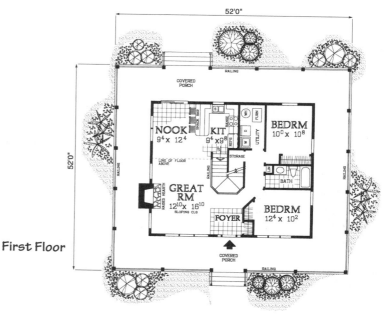

52'0"

COVERED PORCH

RAILING

52'0"

NOOK
9⁴ x 12⁴

KIT
9⁴ x 8⁸

RANGE

REF

UTILITY

FURN

BEDRM
10⁰ x 10⁸

STORAGE

LINE OF FLOOR ABOVE

BATH

GREAT RM
12¹⁰ x 16¹⁰
SLOPING CLG

RAISED HEARTH

FOYER

BEDRM
12⁴ x 10²

COVERED PORCH

RAILING

First Floor

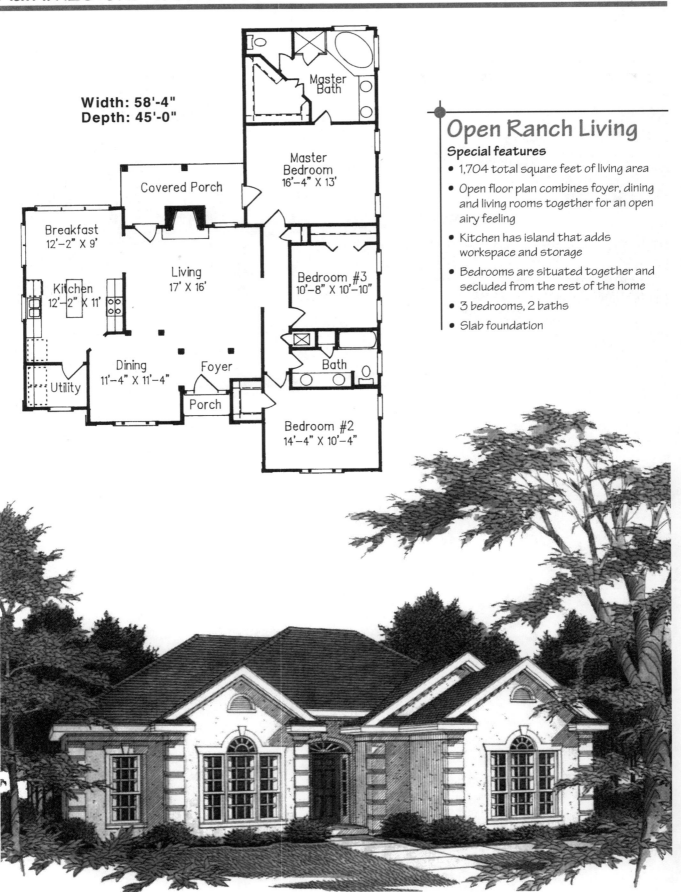

Width: 58'-4"
Depth: 45'-0"

Master Bath

Master Bedroom
16'-4" X 13'

Covered Porch

Breakfast
12'-2" X 9'

Kitchen
12'-2" X 11'

Living
17' X 16'

Bedroom #3
10'-8" X 10'-10"

Dining
11'-4" X 11'-4"

Foyer

Bath

Utility

Porch

Bedroom #2
14'-4" X 10'-4"

Open Ranch Living
Special features

- 1,704 total square feet of living area
- *Open floor plan combines foyer, dining and living rooms together for an open airy feeling*
- Kitchen has island that adds workspace and storage
- *Bedrooms are situated together and secluded from the rest of the home*
- 3 bedrooms, 2 baths
- *Slab foundation*

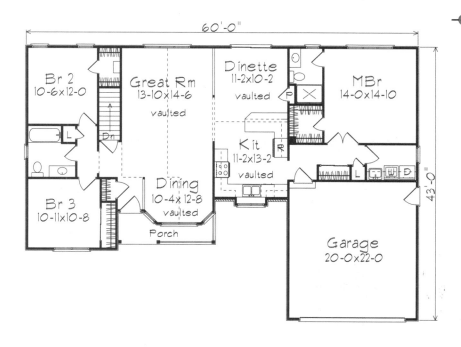

Br 2
10-6x12-0

Great Rm
13-10x14-6
vaulted

Dinette
11-2x10-2
vaulted

MBr
14-0x14-10

Kit
11-2x13-2
vaulted

Dining
10-4x12-8
vaulted

Porch

Br 3
10-11x10-8

Garage
20-0x22-0

60'-0"

43'-0"

Central Living Area Keeps Bedrooms Private

Special features

- 1,546 total square feet of living area
- Spacious, open rooms create casual atmosphere
- Master bedroom is secluded for privacy
- Dining room features large bay window
- Kitchen and dinette combine for added space and include access to the outdoors
- Large laundry room includes convenient sink
- 3 bedrooms, 2 baths, 2-car garage
- Basement foundation

Trio Of Dormers
Adds Curb Appeal

Special features

- 2,126 total square feet of living area
- Hearth room has corner fireplace for warmth
- Great room features entertainment center and a dramatic wall of windows
- Covered front porch is charming
- 3 bedrooms, 2 baths, 2-car side entry garage
- Slab foundation

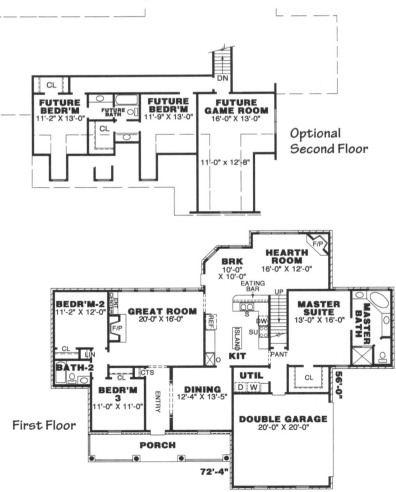

Optional Second Floor

First Floor

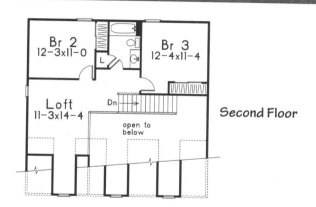

Second Floor

Charming Wrap-Around Porch

Special features

- 1,879 total square feet of living area
- Open floor plan on both floors makes home appear larger
- Loft area overlooks great room or can become an optional fourth bedroom
- Large walk-in pantry in kitchen and large storage in rear of home with access from exterior
- 3 bedrooms, 2 baths
- Crawl space foundation
- 1,314 square feet on the first floor and 565 square feet on the second floor

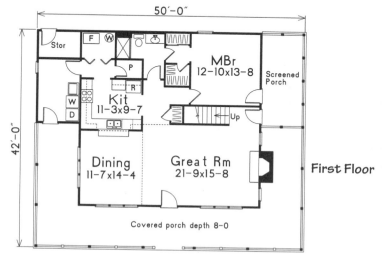

First Floor

Optional Second Floor

BONUS ROOM
21-4 X 12-6

WIDTH 68-10

COPYRIGHT LARRY E. BELK

GARAGE

BRKFST RM
11-4 X 10-6
10 FT CLG

UTIL
10-0 X 10-0

LIN SHLV

42" LEDGE

HIS

MASTER
BATH

KITCHEN
12-0 X 16-0

GREAT ROOM
18-4 X 21-6
12 FT CLG

10 FT CLG

W.K.S

10 FT CLG

BEDROOM 3
13-4 X 12-0
10 FT CLG

DRESSING

BATH 2

LIN

PAN

HERS

DEPTH 77-10

LIN

DRESSING

ARCH ARCH

ARCH

BUILT INS

BEDROOM 2
11-0 X 12-0
10 FT CLG

STUDY/BDRM 4
11-0 X 12-0
12 FT CLG

FOYER
12 FT CLG

DINING ROOM
12-0 X 13-8
12 FT CLG

MASTER BEDROOM
17-0 X 16-4
10 FT CLG

ARCH

PORCH

First Floor

Arches
Add Interest

Special features

- 2,648 total square feet of living area
- 12' ceilings give the study, dining room and great room a larger feel
- Kitchen features a 42' eating bar
- Study off the foyer is an ideal office space with built-in bookshelves
- Optional bonus room has 295 square feet of living area
- 4 bedrooms, 2 baths, 2-car side entry garage
- Basement, crawl space or slab foundation, please specify when ordering

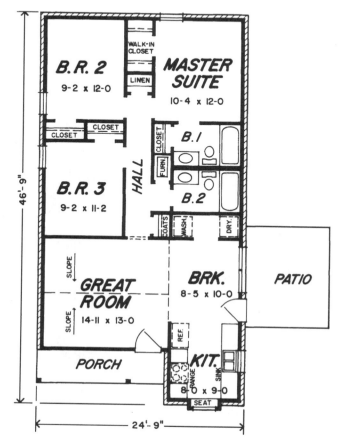

Ideal Home For A Narrow Lot

Special features

- 1,053 total square feet of living area
- Handy utility closet off breakfast room
- Sloped ceiling in great room adds a dramatic touch
- Organized kitchen has everything close by for easy preparation
- 3 bedrooms, 2 baths
- Slab or crawl space foundation, please specify when ordering

Second Floor

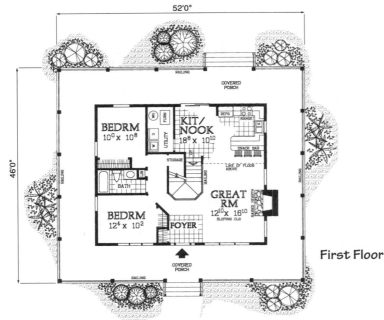

First Floor

A Great Country Farmhouse

Special features

- 1,669 total square feet of living area
- Generous use of windows adds exciting visual elements to the exterior as well as plenty of natural light to the interior
- Two-story great room has a raised hearth
- Second floor loft/study would easily make a terrific home office
- 3 bedrooms, 2 baths
- Crawl space foundation
- 1,093 square feet on the first floor and 576 square feet on the second floor

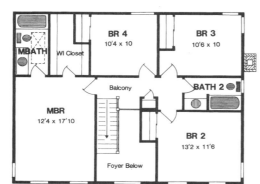

Second Floor

BR 4
10'4 x 10

BR 3
10'6 x 10

MBATH

WI Closet

BATH 2

Balcony

MBR
12'4 x 17'10

BR 2
13'2 x 11'6

Foyer Below

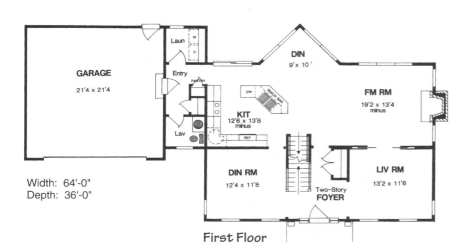

GARAGE
21'4 x 21'4

Laun

Entry

DIN
9' x 10'

FM RM
19'2 x 13'4
minus

KIT
12'6 x 13'8
minus

PANTRY

DW

SNACK BAR

REF

Lav

DIN RM
12'4 x 11'8

Two-Story
FOYER

LIV RM
13'2 x 11'6

Width: 64'-0"
Depth: 36'-0"

First Floor

Great Views
At Rear Of Home

Special features

- 2,050 total square feet of living area
- Angled dining area has lots of windows and opens into family room and kitchen
- All bedrooms located on second floor for privacy from living areas
- Master suite has private bath and a walk-in closet
- 4 bedrooms, 2 1/2 baths, 2-car garage
- Basement foundation
- 1,108 square feet on the first floor and 942 square feet on the second floor

Vaulted Rear Porch

Special features

- 1,849 total square feet of living area
- Open floor plan creates an airy feeling
- Kitchen/breakfast area has center island, pantry and built-in desk
- Master bedroom has private entrance off breakfast area and a view of vaulted porch
- 3 bedrooms, 2 baths, 2-car garage
- Crawl space or slab foundation, please specify when ordering

Width: 66'-5"
Depth: 60'-0"

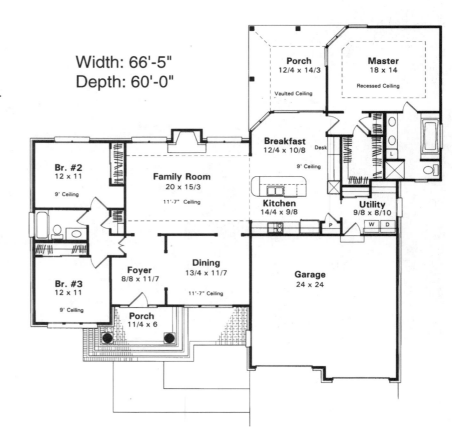

COPYRIGHT LARRY E. BELK

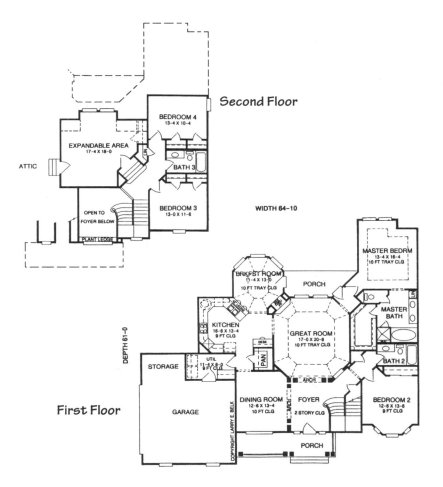

Second Floor

BEDROOM 4
13-4 X 10-4

EXPANDABLE AREA
17-4 X 18-0

ATTIC

BATH 3

OPEN TO
FOYER BELOW

BEDROOM 3
13-0 X 11-6

PLANT LEDGE

WIDTH 64-10

MASTER BEDRM
13-4 X 16-4
10 FT TRAY CLG

BRKFST ROOM
11-4 X 13-0
10 FT TRAY CLG

PORCH

KITCHEN
16-6 X 13-4
9 FT CLG

MASTER
BATH

GREAT ROOM
17-0 X 20-6
10 FT TRAY CLG

UTIL
11-4 X 6-0
8 FT CLG

PAN

DESK

STORAGE

BATH 2

First Floor

GARAGE

DINING ROOM
12-6 X 13-4
10 FT CLG

FOYER
2 STORY CLG

ARCH

BEDROOM 2
12-6 X 13-6
9 FT CLG

DEPTH 61-0

COPYRIGHT LARRY E. BELK

PORCH

Striking
Great Room

Special features

- 2,586 total square feet of living area
- Great room has impressive tray ceiling and see-through fireplace into bayed breakfast room
- Master bedroom has walk-in closet and private bath
- 4 bedrooms, 3 baths, 2-car side entry garage
- Basement, crawl space or slab foundation, please specify when ordering
- 2,028 square feet on the first floor and 558 square feet on the second floor

First Floor

Optional Second Floor

Floor plan labels

- 64'-6"
- 59'-0"
- Bedroom 2 12¹ x 11⁶
- RADIUS WINDOW
- FPL
- RADIUS WINDOW
- FRENCH DOOR
- Breakfast
- PANTRY
- TRAY CEILING
- Sitting Room
- DESK
- Master Suite 15⁰ x 18⁰
- Bath
- LINEN
- Family Room 16⁰ x 19⁶ 13'-5" HIGH CEILING
- PASS THRU
- ISLAND
- DW.
- REF.
- PLANT SHELF ABOVE
- Kitchen
- RANGE
- FRENCH DOOR
- Laund.
- Vaulted M.Bath
- W/D
- K.S.
- SHWR
- Bedroom 3 10⁰ x 11⁰
- OPT. DOOR
- PLANT SHELF ABOVE
- COATS
- Foyer 13'-5" HIGH CEILING
- STAIRS UP
- STAIRS TO OPT. BSMT.
- LINEN
- Living Room / Opt. Bedroom 4 11⁰ x 12²
- W.i.c.
- Dining Room 12¹ x 12⁰ 13'-5" HIGH CEILING
- W.i.c.
- COVERED ENTRY
- Storage
- Garage 21⁰ x 21⁹
- copyright © 1995 frank betz associates, inc.
- W.i.c.
- Bath
- STAIRS DN.
- Opt. Bonus 11⁰ x 20⁰

Kitchen Is A Chef's Dream

Special features

- 2,193 total square feet of living area
- Master suite has sitting room
- Dining room has decorative columns and overlooks family room
- Kitchen has lots of storage
- Optional bonus room with bath on second floor has an additional 400 square feet of living area
- 3 bedrooms, 3 baths, 2-car side entry garage
- Walk-out basement, crawl space or slab foundation, please specify when ordering

Second Floor

Br 5
12-1x14-3

Sunken
Solarium
Below

Br 2
13-11x15-9

Loft

Dn

Br 4
12-1x12-0

Library
15-8x9-8

Br 3
15-5x12-0

open to below

Two-Story Solarium Welcomes The Sun

Special features

- 3,850 total square feet of living area
- Entry, with balcony above, leads into a splendid great room with sunken solarium
- Kitchen layout boasts a half-circle bar and cooktop island with banquet-sized dining nearby
- Solarium features U-shaped stairs with balcony and arched window
- Master suite includes luxurious bath and large study with bay window
- 5 bedrooms, 3 1/2 baths, 3-car garage
- Basement foundation
- 2,306 square feet on the first floor and 1,544 square feet on the second floor

---

First Floor

80'-8"

51'-8"

Patio

Brk

Kit
13-0x9
18-0
vaulted

Hearth Rm
12-1x18-3

Sunken
Solarium

Up Dn

MBr
16-8x13-0

Dining
12-1x16-0

Great Rm
18-0x21-8

Study
16-8x12-3

Garage
30-4x21-4

Entry

Interior View

J.N.HANSEN

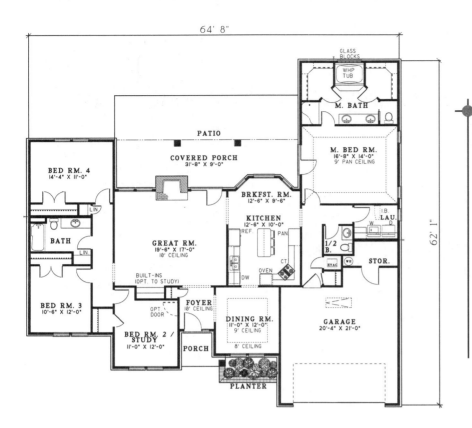

Attractive Exterior

Special features

- 2,107 total square feet of living area
- Master suite separate from other bedrooms for privacy
- Spacious breakfast room and kitchen include center island with eating space
- Centralized great room has fireplace and easy access to any area in the home
- 4 bedrooms, 2 1/2 baths, 2-car garage
- Crawl space, basement, walk-out basement or slab foundation, please specify when ordering

© Michael E. Nelson

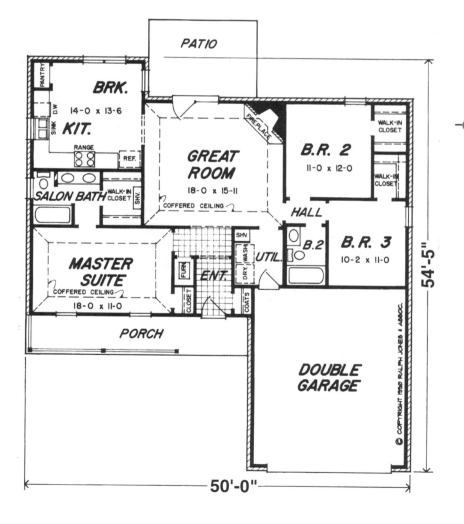

© COPYRIGHT 1990 RALPH JONES & ASSOC.

PATIO

PANTRY

BRK.
14-0 x 13-6

KIT.

SINK   D.W

RANGE

REF.

SALON BATH

WALK-IN CLOSET

SHV.

GREAT ROOM
18-0 x 15-11
COFFERED CEILING

FIREPLACE

B.R. 2
11-0 x 12-0

WALK-IN CLOSET

WALK-IN CLOSET

HALL

MASTER SUITE
COFFERED CEILING
18-0 x 11-0

FURN

ENT.

CLOSET

DRY. WASH.

UTIL.

SHV.

B.2

B.R. 3
10-2 x 11-0

COATS

PORCH

DOUBLE GARAGE

54'-5"

50'-0"

© COPYRIGHT 1990 RALPH JONES & ASSOC.

Terrific Use Of Space

Special features

- 1,436 total square feet of living area
- Corner fireplace in great room warms home
- Kitchen and breakfast room combine for convenience
- Centrally located utility room
- 3 bedrooms, 2 baths, 2-car garage
- Slab foundation

Second Floor

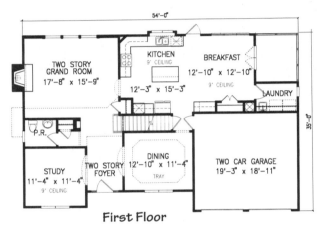

First Floor

Impressive Two-Story Grand Room

Special features

- 2,499 total square feet of living area
- Brick traditional with covered front porch
- Master bedroom has private bath and a sitting room with extra storage
- Impressive two-story foyer
- Kitchen and breakfast room are spacious and have laundry room nearby
- 4 bedrooms, 2 1/2 baths, 2-car garage
- Basement foundation
- 1,257 square feet on the first floor and 1,242 square feet on the second floor

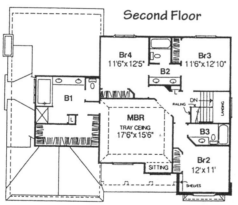

Second Floor

Br4
11'6" x 12'5"

Br3
11'6" x 12'10"

B2

B1

MBR
TRAY CEILING
17'6" x 15'6"

B3

Br2
12' x 11'

SITTING

SHELVES

RAILING DN LANDING

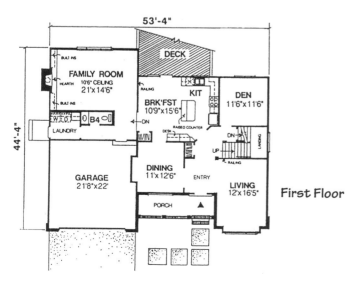

53'-4"

44'-4"

BUILT INS

DECK

FAMILY ROOM
10'6" CEILING
21' x 14'6"

HEARTH

BUILT INS

W.I.C. B4

LAUNDRY

BRK'FST
10'9" x 15'6"

KIT

RAISED COUNTER

DESK

DN

DEN
11'6" x 11'6"

RAILING

DN

UP

RAILING

LANDING

GARAGE
21'8" x 22'

DINING
11' x 12'6"

ENTRY

LIVING
12' x 16'5"

PORCH

First Floor

Terrific Traditional Brick Two-Story

Special features

- 2,900 total square feet of living area

- Master bedroom includes small sitting nook and spacious walk-in closet

- Formal living and dining rooms in the front of the home

- 9' ceilings on first floor

- 4 bedrooms, 3 1/2 baths, 2-car garage

- Basement foundation

- 1,514 square feet on the first floor and 1,386 square feet on the second floor

Second Floor

Private Master Bedroom

Special features

- 2,018 total square feet of living area
- Family room situated near dining area and kitchen create a convenient layout
- First floor master suite features private bath with step-up tub and bay window
- Laundry area located on the first floor
- 4 bedrooms, 2 1/2 baths, 2-car garage
- Basement foundation
- 1,448 square feet on the first floor and 570 square feet on the second floor

First Floor

Width: 48'-0"
Depth: 47'-0"

Cathedral Ceiling In Master Bedroom

Special features

- 2,204 total square feet of living area
- All bedrooms have large walk-in closets
- Great room has fireplace
- Breakfast nook has access outdoors
- 3 bedrooms, 2 baths, 2-car garage
- Basement foundation

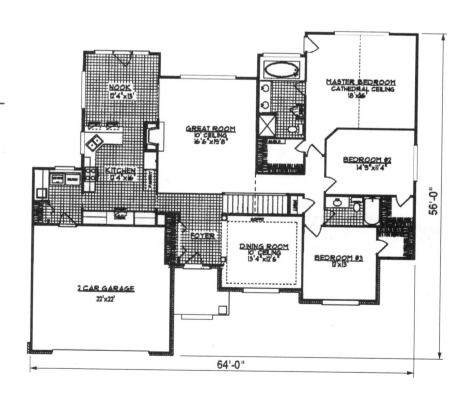

ARTLINE - Kin/Moo
GSDG 2107

Second Floor

VAULTED CEILING LINE

ATTIC STOR.

OPEN TO BELOW

OPEN RAILING

PLANT LEDGE

BEDROOM 2
11-6 × 11-2

STOR.

OPEN RAILING

BATH

PLAYROOM
13-2 × 19-2

OPEN RAILING

BEDROOM 3
11-6 × 12

OPEN TO BELOW

STOR. LINEN

SLOPED CLG

Vaulted Dining Room With Butler's Pantry

Special features

- 2,422 total square feet of living area
- Covered porches invite guests into home
- Convenient and private first floor master suite
- Family room has vaulted ceiling
- 10' ceiling in dining room has formal feel
- Kitchen has walk-in pantry and eating bar
- 3 bedrooms, 2 1/2 baths, 3-car side entry garage
- Crawl space foundation
- 1,495 square feet on the first floor and 927 square feet on the second floor

WIDTH   40'-0"
DEPTH   66'-6"

GARAGE
19-6 × 29-10

COVERED PORCH

FURN

WH

UTIL

FAMILY ROOM
VAULTED CEILING
13-6×14-6

PLANT LEDGE ABOVE

COPYRIGHT 1999 GSDG, INC.

MASTER BATH

PWDR

WALK-IN CLST

UP

NOOK

EATING COUNTER

PHONE DESK

PANTRY

MASTER BEDROOM
13-8×14

ENTRY
OPEN TO ABOVE

BUTLER'S PANTRY

KITCHEN

COVERED PORCH

DINING ROOM
13-4×12-2
VAULTED

TRELLIS

First Floor

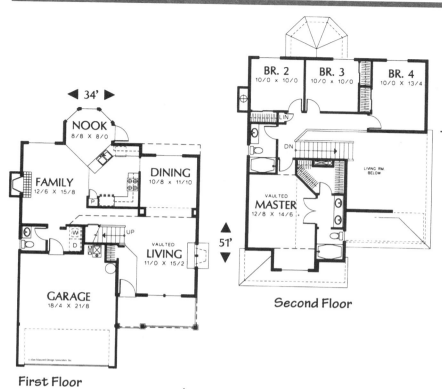

First Floor

NOOK
8/8 X 8/0

FAMILY
12/6 X 15/8

DINING
10/8 x 11/10

VAULTED
LIVING
11/0 X 15/2

GARAGE
18/4 X 21/8

UP

34'

Second Floor

BR. 2
10/0 x 10/0

BR. 3
10/0 x 10/0

BR. 4
10/0 X 13/4

LIN

DN

LIVING RM
BELOW

VAULTED
MASTER
12/8 X 14/6

51'

Nook Brings Outdoors In

Special features

- 1,840 total square feet of living area
- Vaulted living and dining rooms work together when entertaining
- Sunny family room with wall of windows and fireplace
- Second floor has three bedrooms
- Vaulted master suite has private bath
- 4 bedrooms, 2 1/2 baths, 2-car garage
- Crawl space foundation
- 904 square feet on the first floor and 936 square feet on the second floor

Spacious
Country Kitchen

Special features

- 2,184 total square feet of living area

- Delightful family room has access to the screened porch for enjoyable outdoor living

- Secluded master suite is complete with a sitting area and luxurious bath

- Formal living room has double-door entry easily converting it to a study or home office

- Two secondary bedrooms share a full bath

- 3 bedrooms, 3 baths, 2-car side entry garage

- Basement, crawl space or slab foundation, please specify when ordering

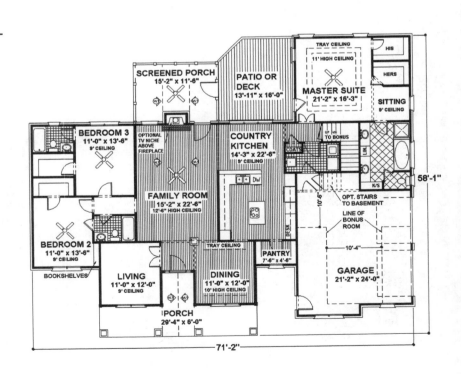

Layout Creates Large Open Living Area

Special features

- 1,285 total square feet of living area
- Accommodating home with ranch-style porch
- Large storage area on back of home
- Master bedroom includes dressing area, private bath and built-in bookcase
- Kitchen features pantry, breakfast bar and complete view to dining room
- 3 bedrooms, 2 baths
- Crawl space foundation, drawings also include basement and slab foundations

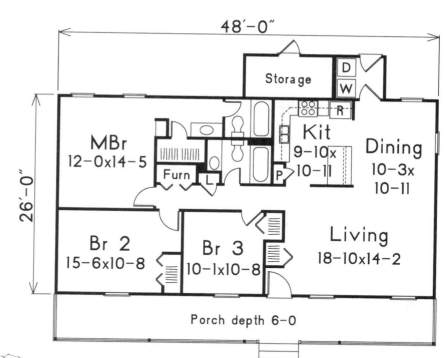

48'-0"

26'-0"

Storage

D
W
R

MBr 12-0x14-5

Furn
L

Kit 9-10x 10-11
P

Dining 10-3x 10-11

Br 2 15-6x10-8

Br 3 10-1x10-8

Living 18-10x14-2

Porch depth 6-0

Traditional Southern Design With Modern Floor Plan

Special features

- 2,214 total square feet of living area
- Great room has built-in cabinets for entertainment system, fireplace and French doors leading to private rear covered porch
- Dining room has an arched opening from foyer
- Breakfast room has lots of windows for a sunny open feel
- 3 bedrooms, 2 baths, 2-car side entry garage
- Crawl space or slab foundation, please specify when ordering

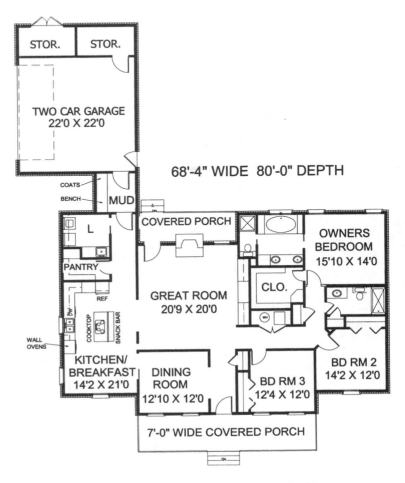

68'-4" WIDE 80'-0" DEPTH

STOR.   STOR.

TWO CAR GARAGE
22'0 X 22'0

COATS
BENCH
MUD

COVERED PORCH

OWNERS BEDROOM
15'10 X 14'0

L

PANTRY

REF

CLO.

GREAT ROOM
20'9 X 20'0

COOKTOP
SNACK BAR

WALL OVENS

KITCHEN/
BREAKFAST
14'2 X 21'0

DINING ROOM
12'10 X 12'0

BD RM 3
12'4 X 12'0

BD RM 2
14'2 X 12'0

7'-0" WIDE COVERED PORCH

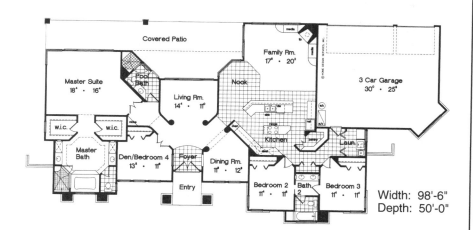

Width: 98'-6"
Depth: 50'-0"

Convenient Pool Bath

Special features

- 2,597 total square feet of living area
- Angled design creates unlimited views and spaces that appear larger
- Den/bedroom #4 makes perfect home office or guest suite
- Island kitchen with view to nook and family room includes walk-in pantry
- Pool bath is shared by outdoor and indoor areas
- 4 bedrooms, 3 baths, 3-car rear entry garage
- Slab foundation

Efficient Floor Plan

Special features

- 1,609 total square feet of living area
- Sunny bay window in breakfast room
- U-shaped kitchen with pantry
- Spacious utility room
- Bedrooms on second floor feature dormers
- Family room includes plenty of space for entertaining
- 3 bedrooms, 2 1/2 baths, 2-car garage
- Slab foundation
- 1,072 square feet on the first floor and 537 square feet on the second floor

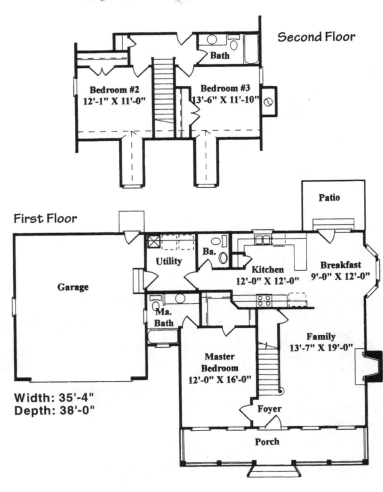

Second Floor

Bath

Bedroom #2
12'-1" X 11'-0"

Bedroom #3
13'-6" X 11'-10"

First Floor

Patio

Utility

Ba.

Kitchen
12'-0" X 12'-0"

Breakfast
9'-0" X 12'-0"

Garage

Ma.
Bath

Family
13'-7" X 19'-0"

Master
Bedroom
12'-0" X 16'-0"

Foyer

Porch

Width: 35'-4"
Depth: 38'-0"

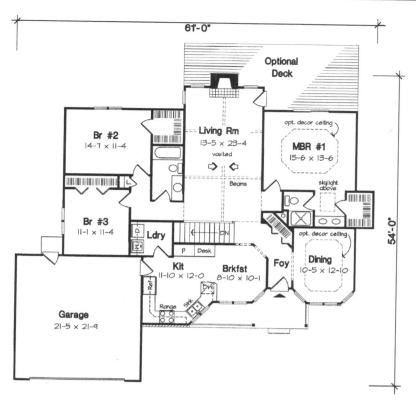

A Ranch With All The Amenities

Special features

- 1,686 total square feet of living area
- Breakfast room surrounded with windows connects to the kitchen for convenience
- Master bedroom separated from secondary bedrooms for privacy
- Vaulted living room features spectacular exposed beams creating a dramatic atmosphere
- 3 bedrooms, 2 baths, 2-car garage
- Basement, crawl space or slab foundation, please specify when ordering

Rear View

Grand Arched Entry

Special features

- 2,564 total square feet of living area
- Hearth room is surrounded by kitchen, dining and breakfast rooms making it the focal point of the living areas
- Escape to the master bedroom which has a luxurious private bath and a sitting area leading to the deck outdoors
- The secondary bedrooms share a jack and jill bath and both have walk-in closets
- 3 bedrooms, 2 1/2 baths, 2-car side entry garage
- Basement, crawl space or slab foundation, please specify when ordering

Second Floor

First Floor

Stone Accents The Front Facade

Special features

- 2,089 total square feet of living area
- First floor garden solarium
- 9' ceilings on first floor
- Energy efficient home with 2" x 6" exterior walls
- 3 bedrooms, 2 1/2 baths, 2-car side entry garage
- Basement foundation
- 1,146 square feet on the first floor and 943 square feet on the second floor

Lovely Entry Highlighted With Large Window

Special features

- 2,310 total square feet of living area
- 9' ceilings on first floor
- Fireplace in great room is flanked by windows creating a sunny atmosphere
- Large playroom on second floor is convenient to secondary bedrooms
- Second floor utility room provides convenience
- 3 bedrooms, 2 1/2 baths, 2-car garage
- Slab foundation
- 1,013 square feet on the first floor and 1,297 square feet on the second floor

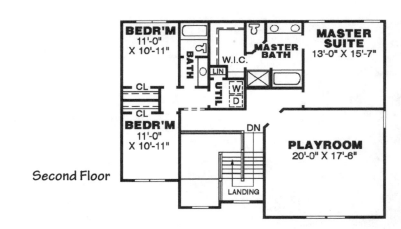

Second Floor

BEDR'M 11'-0" X 10'-11"
BATH
MASTER BATH
W.I.C.
MASTER SUITE 13'-0" X 15'-7"
CL
LIN
UTIL
W/D
CL
BEDR'M 11'-0" X 10'-11"
DN
PLAYROOM 20'-0" X 17'-6"
LANDING

First Floor

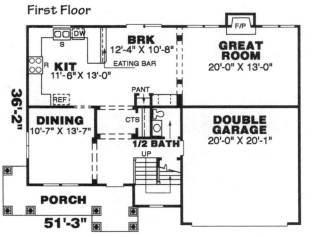

DW
S
R
KIT 11'-6" X 13'-0"
BRK 12'-4" X 10'-8"
EATING BAR
F/P
GREAT ROOM 20'-0" X 13'-0"
REF
PANT
CTS
36'-2"
DINING 10'-7" X 13'-7"
1/2 BATH
DOUBLE GARAGE 20'-0" X 20'-1"
UP
PORCH
51'-3"

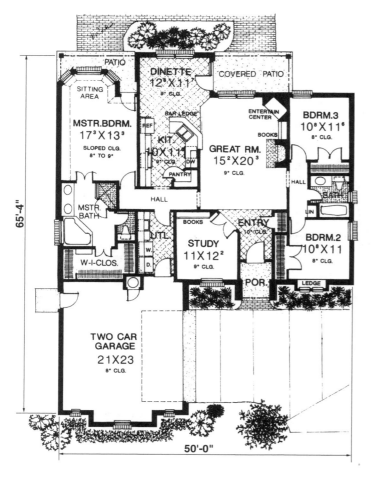

Study Off Main Entrance

Special features

- 1,760 total square feet of living area
- Stone and brick exterior has old world charm
- Master suite includes a sitting area and is situated away from other bedrooms for privacy
- Kitchen and dinette access the outdoors
- Great room includes fireplace, built-in bookshelves and entertainment center
- 3 bedrooms, 2 baths, 2-car side entry garage
- Slab foundation

Fabulous Curb Appeal

Special features

- 1,588 total square feet of living area
- Workshop in garage ideal for storage and projects
- 12' vaulted master suite has his and hers closets as well as a lovely bath with bayed soaking tub and compartmentalized shower and toilet area
- Lovely arched entry to 14' vaulted great room that flows open to the dining room and sky-lit kitchen
- 3 bedrooms, 2 baths, 2-car garage
- Basement foundation

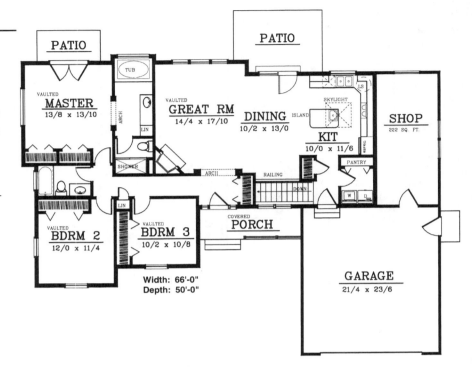

Width: 66'-0"
Depth: 50'-0"

Efficient Kitchen

Special features

- 2,382 total square feet of living area
- Varied ceiling heights throughout
- Interesting master bedroom layout has French doors leading into luxurious master bath
- Two-way fireplace warms living and family rooms
- 4 bedrooms, 2 baths, 2-car side entry garage with storage
- Slab foundation

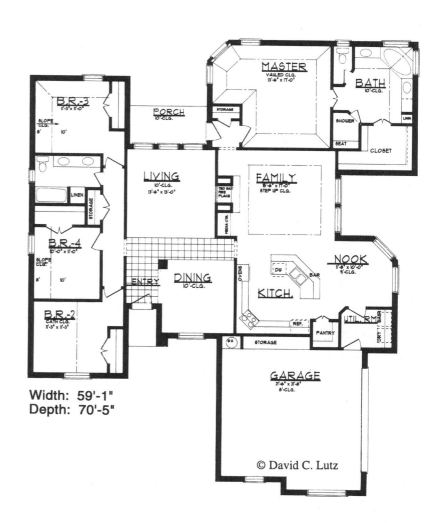

Width: 59'-1"
Depth: 70'-5"

© David C. Lutz

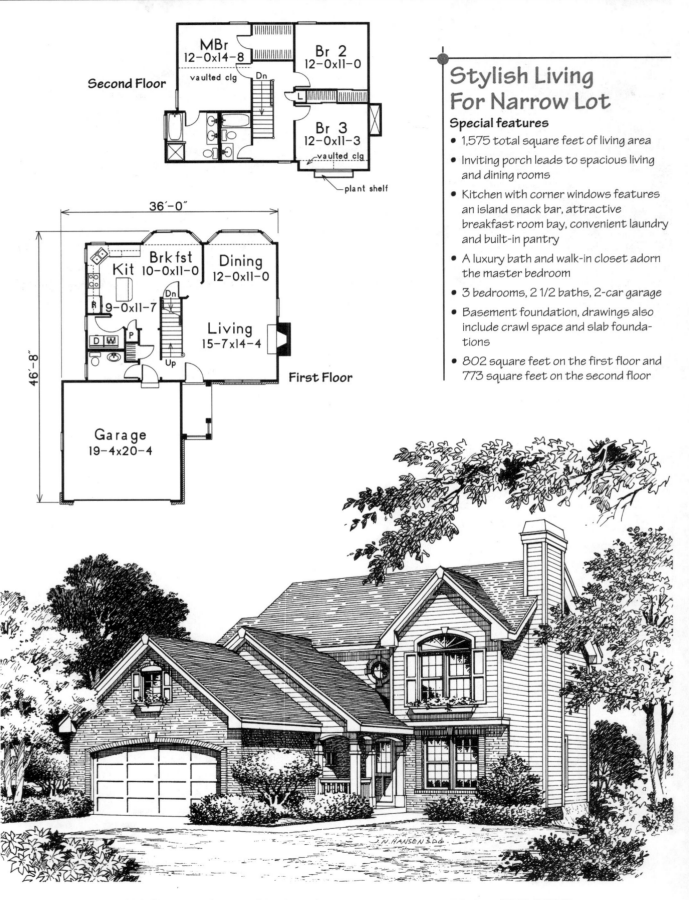

Second Floor

MBr
12-0x14-8
vaulted clg

Br 2
12-0x11-0

Dn

Br 3
12-0x11-3
vaulted clg

plant shelf

36'-0"

46'-8"

Kit
9-0x11-7

Brk fst
10-0x11-0

Dining
12-0x11-0

Dn

Living
15-7x14-4

Up

First Floor

Garage
19-4x20-4

Stylish Living For Narrow Lot

Special features

- 1,575 total square feet of living area

- Inviting porch leads to spacious living and dining rooms

- Kitchen with corner windows features an island snack bar, attractive breakfast room bay, convenient laundry and built-in pantry

- A luxury bath and walk-in closet adorn the master bedroom

- 3 bedrooms, 2 1/2 baths, 2-car garage

- Basement foundation, drawings also include crawl space and slab foundations

- 802 square feet on the first floor and 773 square feet on the second floor

J.N. HANSEN 3.06

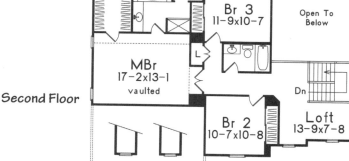

Second Floor

Br 3
11-9x10-7

Open To
Below

MBr
17-2x13-1
vaulted

L

Dn

Loft
13-9x7-8

Br 2
10-7x10-8

Timeless
Country Facade

Special features

- 1,977 total square feet of living area

- An enormous entry with adjacent dining area and powder room leads to a splendid two-story family room with fireplace

- Kitchen features an abundance of cabinets, built-in pantry and breakfast room with menu desk and bay window

- A spacious vaulted master suite, two secondary bedrooms with bath and loft area adorn the second floor

- 3 bedrooms, 2 1/2 baths, 2-car garage with storage area

- Basement foundation

- 977 square feet on the first floor and 1,000 square feet on the second floor

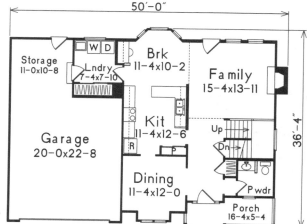

50'-0"

Storage
11-0x10-8

W D

Brk
11-4x10-2

Lndry
7-4x7-10

Family
15-4x13-11

Garage
20-0x22-8

Kit
11-4x12-6

Up

R

Dn

36'-4"

P

Dining
11-4x12-0

Pwdr

Porch
16-4x5-4

First Floor

Our Blueprint Packages Offer...

Quality plans for building your future, with extras that provide unsurpassed value, ensure good construction and long-term enjoyment.

A quality home - one that looks good, functions well, and provides years of enjoyment - is a product of many things - design, materials, craftsmanship. But it's also the result of outstanding blueprints - the actual plans and specifications that tell the builder exactly how to build your home.

And with our BLUEPRINT PACKAGES you get the absolute best. A complete set of blueprints is available for every design in this book. These "working drawings," are highly detailed, resulting in two key benefits:

   n Better understanding by the contractor of how to build your home, and...

   n More accurate construction estimates.

When you purchase one of our designs, you'll receive all of the BLUEPRINT components shown here - elevations, foundation plan, floor plans, sections and/or details. Other helpful building aids are also available to help make your dream home a reality.

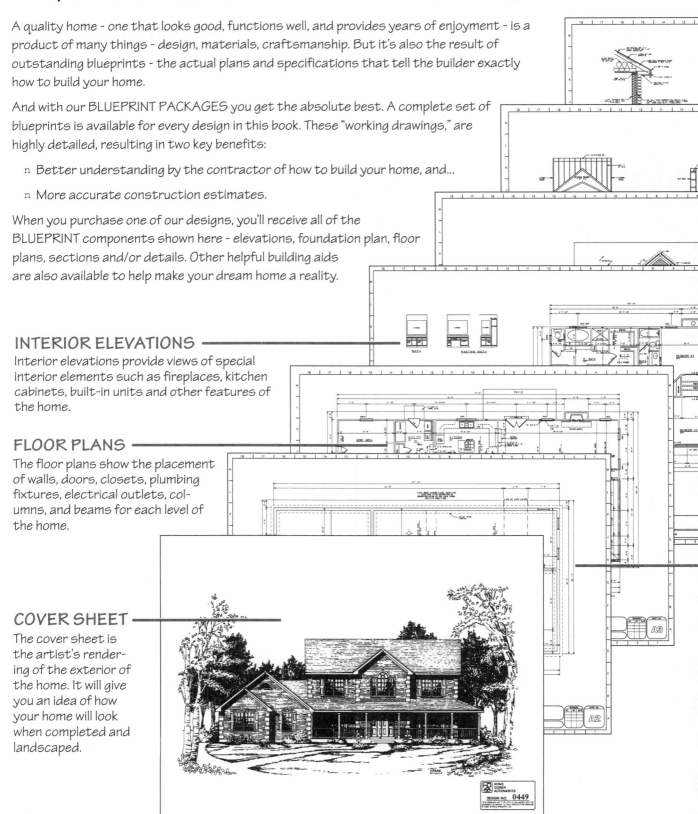

INTERIOR ELEVATIONS
Interior elevations provide views of special interior elements such as fireplaces, kitchen cabinets, built-in units and other features of the home.

FLOOR PLANS
The floor plans show the placement of walls, doors, closets, plumbing fixtures, electrical outlets, columns, and beams for each level of the home.

COVER SHEET
The cover sheet is the artist's rendering of the exterior of the home. It will give you an idea of how your home will look when completed and landscaped.

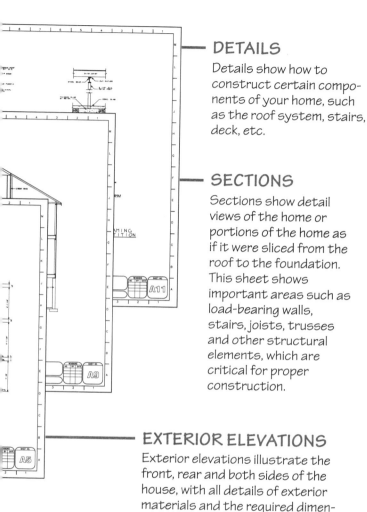

DETAILS

Details show how to construct certain components of your home, such as the roof system, stairs, deck, etc.

SECTIONS

Sections show detail views of the home or portions of the home as if it were sliced from the roof to the foundation. This sheet shows important areas such as load-bearing walls, stairs, joists, trusses and other structural elements, which are critical for proper construction.

EXTERIOR ELEVATIONS

Exterior elevations illustrate the front, rear and both sides of the house, with all details of exterior materials and the required dimensions.

FOUNDATION PLAN

The foundation plan shows the layout of the basement, crawl space, slab or pier foundation. All necessary notations and dimensions are included. See plan page for the foundation types included. If the home plan you choose does not have your desired foundation type, our Customer Service Representatives can advise you on how to customize your foundation to suit your specific needs or site conditions.

Other Helpful Building Aids...

Your Blueprint Package will contain the necessary construction information to build your home. We also offer the following products and services to save you time and money in the building process.

MATERIAL LIST

Material lists are available for many of the plans in this book. Each list gives you the quantity, dimensions and description of the building materials necessary to construct your home. You'll get faster and more accurate bids from your contractor while saving money by paying for only the materials you need. See the Home Plans Index on pages 318-319 for availability and pricing.

DETAIL PLAN PACKAGES:

Framing, Plumbing & Electrical Plan Packages

Three separate packages offer homebuilders details for constructing various foundations; numerous floor, wall and roof framing techniques; simple to complex residential wiring; sump and water softener hookups; plumbing connection methods; installation of septic systems and more. Each package includes three-dimensional illustrations and a glossary of terms. Purchase one or all three. Cost: $20.00 each or all three for $40.00. Note: These drawings do not pertain to a specific floor plan.

THE LEGAL KIT ™

Our Legal Kit provides contracts and legal forms to help protect you from the potential pitfalls inherent in the building process. The Kit supplies commonly used forms and contracts suitable for homeowners and builders. It can save you a considerable amount of time and help protect you and your assets during and after construction. Cost: $35.00

EXPRESS DELIVERY

Most orders are processed within 24 hours of receipt. Please allow 7-10 business days for delivery. If you need to place a rush order, please call us by 11:00 a.m. Monday-Friday CST and ask for express service (allow 1-2 business days).

TECHNICAL ASSISTANCE

If you have questions, call our technical support line at 1-314-770-2228 between 8:00 a.m. and 5:00 p.m. Monday-Friday CST. Whether it involves design modifications or field assistance, our designers are extremely familiar with all of our designs and will be happy to help you. We want your home to be everything you expect it to be.

 **HOME DESIGN ALTERNATIVES, INC.**

Plan #	Sq. Ft.	Price Code	Page	Mat. List Price
X26-0101	1,039	AA	86	X/$55.00
X26-0102	1,246	A	142	X/$60.00
X26-0112	1,668	C	15	X/$70.00
X26-0151	2,874	E	149	X/$70.00
X26-0159	3,368	F	124	X/$70.00
X26-0161	1,630	B	45	X/$60.00
X26-0173	1,220	A	145	X/$60.00
X26-0174	1,657	B	116	X/$60.00
X26-0190	1,600	C	12	X/$65.00
X26-0191	1,868	D	76	X/$65.00
X26-0203	1,475	B	10	X/$60.00
X26-0217	1,360	A	152	X/$60.00
X26-0219	3,222	F	103	X/$70.00
X26-0227	1,674	B	265	X/$60.00
X26-0229	1,676	B	211	X/$60.00
X26-0230	2,073	D	57	X/$65.00
X26-0249	1,501	B	205	X/$60.00
X26-0352	3,144	E	216	X/$70.00
X26-0354	2,597	E	260	X/$65.00
X26-0355	3,814	G	155	X/$60.00
X26-0370	1,721	C	5	X/$65.00
X26-0382	1,546	C	283	X/$60.00
X26-0413	2,182	D	64	X/$65.00
X26-0417	2,828	F	163	X/$70.00
X26-0418	3,850	F	293	X/$70.00
X26-0434	2,357	D	150	X/$65.00
X26-0448	1,597	C	146	X/$65.00
X26-0449	2,505	D	11	X/$65.00
X26-0450	1,708	B	147	X/$60.00
X26-0477	1,140	AA	58	X/$55.00
X26-0488	2,059	C	160	X/$65.00
X26-0521	2,050	C	148	X/$65.00
X26-0529	1,285	B	303	X/$60.00
X26-0657	914	AA	153	X/$55.00
X26-0670	1,170	AA	213	X/$55.00
X26-0690	1,400	B	6	X/$60.00
X26-0702	1,558	B	36	X/$60.00
X26-0705	2,758	E	54	X/$70.00
X26-0706	1,791	C	3	X/$60.00
X26-0707	2,723	E	24	X/$70.00
X26-0708	2,615	E	136	X/$70.00
X26-0711	1,575	B	314	X/$60.00
X26-0712	2,029	D	13	X/$65.00
X26-0715	4,826	G	70	X/$75.00
X26-0717	1,268	B	154	X/$60.00
X26-0721	2,437	D	243	X/$65.00
X26-0725	1,977	C	315	X/$65.00
X26-0726	1,428	A	122	X/$60.00
X26-0728	2,967	E	7	X/$70.00
X26-0732	1,384	B	8	X/$60.00
X26-0736	2,900	E	9	X/$70.00
X26-0739	1,684	B	157	X/$60.00
X26-0745	1,819	C	245	X/$65.00
X26-0747	1,977	C	151	X/$65.00
X26-0749	2,727	E	158	X/$70.00
X26-0755	1,787	B	4	X/$60.00
X26-0759	2,125	C	14	X/$65.00
X26-0768	1,879	C	285	X/$65.00
X26-0784	3,556	F	83	X/$70.00
X26-0790	2,397	D	16	X/$65.00
X26-0794	1,433	A	192	X/$60.00
X26-0796	1,599	B	231	X/$60.00
X26-0798	2,128	C	252	X/$65.00
X26-0801	2,544	D	46	X/$65.00
X26-0803	3,366	F	273	X/$70.00
X26-0804	2,795	E	179	X/$70.00
X26-0805	2,750	E	111	X/$70.00
X26-0807	1,231	A	159	X/$60.00
X26-0809	1,084	AA	156	X/$55.00
X26-0821	2,695	E	174	X/$70.00
X26-AMD-1135	1,467	A	275	X/$125.00
X26-AMD-1213	2,197	C	102	X/$125.00
X26-AMD-2120C	1,893	C	74	
X26-AMD-2146J	1,840	C	301	X/$125.00
X26-AMD-2157L	1,548	B	232	
X26-AMD-2163	1,978	C	38	X/$125.00
X26-AMD-2175	1,464	A	180	X/$125.00
X26-AMD-2294	2,391	D	238	X/$125.00
X26-AP-1002	1,050	AA	261	
X26-AP-1612	1,643	B	235	
X26-AP-1717	1,787	B	22	
X26-AP-1911	1,992	C	104	X/$125.00
X26-AP-1914	1,992	C	217	X/$125.00
X26-AP-2018	2,088	C	130	
X26-AP-2020	2,097	C	276	
X26-AP-2119	2,184	C	302	
X26-AP-2220	2,288	D	110	
X26-AP-2317	2,340	D	167	
X26-AP-2416	2,484	D	228	
X26-AP-2520	2,564	D	308	
X26-AX-4315	2,018	C	91	X/$125.00
X26-AX-5378	1,897	C	120	X/$125.00
X26-AX-5380	1,480	A	181	X/$125.00
X26-AX-7944	1,648	B	226	X/$125.00
X26-AX-90303	1,615	B	271	X/$125.00
X26-AX-95367	1,595	B	264	X/$125.00
X26-BF-1416	1,434	A	47	X/$125.00
X26-BF-1426	1,420	A	82	X/$125.00
X26-BF-1711	1,770	B	140	X/$125.00
X26-BF-1828	1,828	C	187	X/$125.00
X26-BF-1901	1,925	C	268	X/$125.00
X26-BF-2107	2,123	E	237	X/$125.00
X26-BF-2108	2,194	C	263	X/$125.00
X26-BF-3007	3,012	E	42	X/$125.00
X26-BF-DR1108	1,150	AA	244	X/$125.00
X26-BF-DR1109	1,191	AA	114	X/$125.00
X26-CHD-11-27	1,123	AA	19	
X26-CHD-13-61	1,379	A	60	
X26-CHD-16-10	1,680	B	162	
X26-CHD-16-41	1,634	B	218	
X26-CHD-18-53	2,310	D	310	
X26-CHD-20-51	2,084	C	132	
X26-CHD-21-58	2,126	C	284	
X26-CHD-23-10	2,350	D	240	
X26-CHD-24-53	2,414	D	106	
X26-CHD-27-35	2,743	E	194	
X26-CHD-29-58	3,369	F	71	
X26-CHP-1532-A-141	1,500	B	197	
X26-CHP-1633-A-25	1,609	B	306	
X26-CHP-1732-A-101	1,704	B	282	
X26-CHP-1733-A-7	1,737	B	85	
X26-CHP-2132B	2,172	C	28	
X26-CHP-2233-B-21	2,697	E	141	
X26-CHP-2444-A-2	2,473	D	215	
X26-CHP-2543-A-42	2,500	D	90	
X26-DBI-1748-19	1,911	C	52	X/$125.00
X26-DBI-2285	2,115	C	41	X/$125.00
X26-DBI-2311	2,486	D	59	X/$125.00
X26-DBI-2461	1,850	C	65	X/$125.00
X26-DBI-2619	1,998	C	63	X/$125.00
X26-DBI-2701	2,340	D	225	X/$125.00
X26-DBI-2839	3,057	E	247	X/$125.00
X26-DBI-3019	1,479	A	270	X/$125.00
X26-DBI-4144	3,040	E	257	X/$125.00
X26-DBI-5498	2,188	C	279	X/$125.00
X26-DBI-8013	1,392	A	161	X/$125.00
X26-DDI-92-101	1,785	B	56	X/$125.00
X26-DDI-92-501	1,742	B	204	
X26-DDI-95219	1,251	A	214	
X26-DDI-97-207	2,534	D	96	
X26-DDI-98-106	1,588	B	312	
X26-DDI-98-203	2,504	D	236	
X26-DDI-100214	2,104	C	137	
X26-DH-864G	864	AAA	138	
X26-DH-1716	1,716	B	72	
X26-DH-1786	1,785	B	166	
X26-DH-2005	1,700	B	134	
X26-DH-2052	2,052	C	121	
X26-DH-2108	2,156	C	254	
X26-DH-2214	2,214	D	304	
X26-DH-2340	2,340	D	17	
X26-DH-2600	2,669	E	272	
X26-DH-2726	2,726	E	184	
X26-DL-16653L1	1,665	B	18	
X26-DL-17353L1	1,735	B	87	
X26-DL-20604L2	2,060	C	139	
X26-DL-23824L2	2,382	C	313	
X26-DL-25454L1	2,545	D	229	
X26-DR-1478	920	AA	20	X/$125.00
X26-DR-2686	1,995	C	84	X/$125.00
X26-DR-2688	1,922	C	94	X/$125.00
X26-DR-2801	1,760	B	182	X/$125.00
X26-DR-2835	1,976	C	234	X/$125.00
X26-DR-2837	2,300	D	118	X/$125.00
X26-DR-2853	2,089	C	309	X/$125.00
X26-DR-2884	2,135	C	241	X/$125.00
X26-DR-2891	2,310	D	123	X/$125.00
X26-DR-2896	1,938	C	201	X/$125.00
X26-DR-2940	1,482	A	177	X/$125.00
X26-FB-174	2,115	C	119	X/$125.00
X26-FB-543	1,945	C	21	X/$125.00
X26-FB-698	2,352	D	73	X/$125.00
X26-FB-845	1,779	B	135	X/$125.00
X26-FB-851	2,349	D	185	X/$125.00
X26-FB-902	1,856	C	253	X/$125.00
X26-FB-930	2,322	D	105	X/$125.00
X26-FB-933	2,193	C	292	X/$125.00
X26-FB-960	2,201	D	183	X/$125.00
X26-FB-963	2,126	C	115	X/$125.00
X26-FDG-7963-L	1,830	C	26	
X26-FDG-8378-L	2,591	D	77	
X26-FDG-8575-L	2,793	E	125	
X26-FDG-8576-L	3,017	E	170	
X26-FDG-8701-L	2,578	D	219	
X26-FDG-8753-L	2,674	E	262	
X26-FDG-9035	1,760	B	311	
X26-GH-20083	1,575	B	112	X/$125.00
X26-GH-24326	1,505	B	40	X/$125.00
X26-GH-24706	1,470	A	200	X/$125.00
X26-GH-24717	1,642	B	248	X/$125.00
X26-GH-24724	1,982	C	133	X/$125.00
X26-GH-24736	2,044	C	258	
X26-GH-34029	1,686	B	307	X/$125.00
X26-GH-34043	1,583	B	206	
X26-GH-34901	1,763	B	186	
X26-GM-1253	1,253	A	92	X/$125.00
X26-GM-1388	1,388	A	23	X/$125.00
X26-GM-1406	1,406	A	143	X/$125.00
X26-GM-1780	1,780	B	202	X/$125.00
X26-GM-1849	1,849	C	290	X/$125.00
X26-GM-1855	1,855	C	171	
X26-GM-1966	1,966	C	144	X/$125.00
X26-GM-2008	2,008	C	195	X/$125.00
X26-GM-2010	2,010	C	249	
X26-GM-2148	2,148	C	239	X/$125.00

Home Plans Index

Plan #	Sq. Ft.	Price Code	Page	Mat. List Price
X26-GSD-1001	3,158	E	33	
X26-GSD-1123	1,734	B	176	
X26-GSD-1748	1,496	A	210	
X26-GSD-2004	1,751	B	128	
X26-GSD-2107	2,422	D	300	
X26-HDS-1758	1,783	B	25	X/$125.00
X26-HDS-1817	1,817	C	75	
X26-HDS-2140	2,140	C	117	X/$125.00
X26-HDS-2221-2	2,221	D	178	
X26-HDS-2224	2,224	D	203	X/$125.00
X26-HDS-2551	2,551	D	50	
X26-HDS-2597	2,597	D	305	X/$125.00
X26-HDS-2962	2,962	E	277	X/$125.00
X26-HDS-3436	3,436	F	175	X/$125.00
X26-HDS-3556	3,556	F	196	X/$125.00
X26-HP-B947	1,830	C	30	X/$125.00
X26-HP-C316	1,997	C	51	X/$125.00
X26-HP-C460	1,389	A	98	X/$125.00
X26-HP-C619	1,771	B	173	X/$125.00
X26-HP-C662	1,937	C	223	X/$125.00
X26-HP-C675	1,673	B	281	X/$125.00
X26-HP-C681	1,669	B	288	X/$125.00
X26-HP-C689	1,295	A	164	X/$125.00
X26-JA52194	1,802	C	48	
X26-JA52694	2,042	C	89	
X26-JA53594	1,730	B	131	X/$125.00
X26-JA53994	2,204	D	299	
X26-JA-55294	1,986	C	259	
X26-JA-61495	1,540	B	230	X/$125.00
X26-JA-64396	2,196	C	191	X/$125.00
X26-JA-77598	1,600	C	126	
X26-JFD-20-1868-1	1,868	C	31	
X26-JFD-20-1873-1	1,873	C	88	X/$125.00
X26-JFD-20-1887-1	1,887	C	168	
X26-JFD-20-1992-1	1,992	C	233	
X26-JFD-20-2018-1	2,018	C	298	
X26-JFD-20-2050-1	2,050	C	289	
X26-JFD-20-2211-1	2,211	D	190	
X26-JV-1268A	1,268	A	27	
X26-JV-1325-B	1,325	A	66	X/$125.00
X26-JV-1675-A	1,675	B	108	
X26-JV-1716-A	1,716	B	100	X/$125.00
X26-JV-1735A	1,735	B	198	X/$125.00
X26-JV-1765-A-SJ	1,765	B	269	X/$125.00
X26-JV-1869-A	1,869	C	280	X/$125.00
X26-JV-1870-A	1,870	C	220	X/$125.00
X26-JV-2091-A	2,475	D	80	X/$125.00
X26-JV-2788-A	2,788	E	208	
X26-LBD-13-1A	1,310	A	32	
X26-LBD-18-5A	1,862	C	109	
X26-LBD-18-11A	1,890	C	67	
X26-LBD-19-23A	1,932	C	188	
X26-LBD-25-22A	2,586	D	291	
X26-LBD-26-21A	2,648	E	286	
X26-LBD-26-23A	2,678	E	221	
X26-LBD-26-24A	2,611	E	224	
X26-MG-9305	1,606	B	99	
X26-MG-9510	2,379	D	29	
X26-MG-9519-B	2,323	D	79	
X26-MG-95107	3,029	E	222	
X26-MG-96108	2,499	D	296	
X26-MG-96132	2,450	D	256	
X26-MG-96151	3,422	F	199	
X26-MG-96216	2,696	E	113	
X26-NDG-110	2,092	C	37	X/$125.00
X26-NDG-111	2,698	E	81	
X26-NDG-113-1	1,525	B	62	
X26-NDG-118	2,502	D	250	
X26-NDG-142	2,107	C	49	
X26-NDG-145-2	1,680	B	266	X/$125.00
X26-NDG-190	2,107	C	294	
X26-NDG-204	2,439	D	246	
X26-NDG-275	2,247	D	255	
X26-NDG-347	1,957	C	274	
X26-RDD-1374-9	1,374	A	267	
X26-RDD-1429-9	1,429	A	55	
X26-RDD-1753-9	1,753	B	169	
X26-RDD-1791-9	1,791	B	101	
X26-RDD-1815-8	1,815	C	93	
X26-RDD-1896-9	1,896	C	251	
X26-RDD-2050-7A	2,050	C	209	
X26-RJ-A1068V	1,053	AA	287	
X26-RJ-A1079	1,021	AA	207	
X26-RJ-A1175	1,192	AA	35	
X26-RJ-A1293	1,253	A	43	
X26-RJ-A1485	1,436	A	295	
X26-RJ-A1491	1,482	A	68	
X26-RJ-B123	1,270	A	127	
X26-RJ-B1416	1,455	A	212	
X26-SH-SEA-008	1,073	AA	53	X/$125.00
X26-SH-SEA-025	1,018	AA	39	X/$125.00
X26-SH-SEA-028	1,404	A	44	X/$125.00
X26-SH-SEA-091	1,541	B	95	X/$125.00
X26-SH-SEA-100	2,582	D	97	X/$125.00
X26-SH-SEA-101	2,750	E	189	X/$125.00
X26-SH-SEA-208	2,516	D	165	X/$125.00
X26-SH-SEA-225	1,230	A	278	X/$125.00
X26-SH-SEA-242	1,408	A	69	X/$125.00
X26-SH-SEA-298	1,405	A	227	X/$125.00
X26-SH-SEA-302	1,375	A	78	X/$125.00
X26-SH-SEA-305	1,924	C	61	X/$125.00
X26-UDG-92007	1,753	B	129	
X26-UDG-93001	2,003	C	193	
X26-UDG-97001	2,316	D	107	
X26-UDG-97008	2,086	C	242	
X26-UDG-97010	2,900	E	297	
X26-UDG-99011	2,900	E	172	
X26-UDG-99003	1,425	A	34	

What Kind Of Plan Package Do You Need?

Now that you've found the home you've been looking for, here are some suggestions on how to make your Dream Home a reality. To get started, order the type of plans that fit your particular situation.

YOUR CHOICES:

The 1-Set Study package - We offer a 1-set plan package so you can study your home in detail. This one set is considered a study set and is marked "not for construction." It is a copyright violation to reproduce blueprints.

The Minimum 5-Set package - If you're ready to start the construction process, this 5-set package is the minimum number of blueprint sets you will need. It will require keeping close track of each set so they can be used by multiple subcontractors and tradespeople.

The Standard 8-set package - For best results in terms of cost, schedule and quality of construction, we recommend you order eight (or more) sets of blueprints. Besides one set for yourself, additional sets of blueprints will be required by your mortgage lender, local building department, general contractor and all subcontractors working on foundation, electrical, plumbing, heating/air conditioning, carpentry work, etc.

Reproducible Masters - If you wish to make some minor design changes, you'll want to order reproducible masters. These drawings contain the same information as the blueprints but are printed on erasable and reproducible paper. This will allow your builder or a local design professional to make the necessary drawing changes without the major expense of redrawing the plans. This package also allows you to print as many copies of the modified plans as you need.

Mirror Reverse Sets - Plans can be printed in mirror reverse. These plans are useful when the house would fit your site better if all the rooms were on the opposite side than shown. They are simply a mirror image of the original drawings causing the lettering and dimensions to read backwards. Therefore, when ordering mirror reverse drawings, you must purchase at least one set of right reading plans.

How To Order

For fastest service, Call Toll-Free
1-800-DREAM HOME
(1-800-373-2646) day or night

Three Easy Ways To Order

1. CALL toll free 1-800-373-2646 for credit card orders. MasterCard, Visa, Discover and American Express are accepted.

2. FAX your order to 1-314-770-2226.

3. MAIL the Order Form to:

   HDA, Inc.
   4390 Green Ash Drive
   St. Louis, MO 63045

ORDER FORM

Please send me -

PLAN NUMBER X26-_____

PRICE CODE _____ (see Plan Index)

Specify Foundation Type - see plan page for availability
☐ Slab ☐ Crawl space ☐ Pier
☐ Basement ☐ Walk-out basement

☐ Reproducible Masters	$ _____
☐ Eight-Set Plan Package	$ _____
☐ Five-Set Plan Package	$ _____
☐ One-Set Study Package (no mirror reverse)	$ _____
☐ Additional Plan Sets _____ (Qty.) at $45.00 each	$ _____
☐ Print in Mirror Reverse _____ (Qty.) add $15.00 per set	$ _____
☐ Material List (see pages 318-319)	$ _____
☐ Legal Kit (see page 317)	$ _____
Detail Plan Packages: (see page 317) ☐ Framing ☐ Electrical ☐ Plumbing	$ _____
SUBTOTAL	$ _____
SALES TAX (MO residents add 6%)	$ _____
☐ Shipping / Handling (see chart at right)	$ _____
TOTAL ENCLOSED (US funds only) *(Sorry no CODs)*	$ _____

I hereby authorize HDA, Inc. to charge this purchase to my credit card account (check one):

☐ MasterCard ☐ VISA ☐ DISCOVER NOVUS ☐ AMERICAN EXPRESS Cards

Credit Card number_____

Expiration date _____

Signature_____

Name_____
(Please print or type)

Street Address _____
*(Please **do not** use PO Box)*

City _____

State _____ Zip _____

Daytime phone number (_____) - _____

I'm a ☐ Builder/Contractor
☐ Homeowner
☐ Renter
I ☐ have
☐ have not
selected my
general contractor

Thank you for your order!
320

IMPORTANT INFORMATION TO KNOW BEFORE YOU ORDER

◆ **Exchange Policies** - Since blueprints are printed in response to your order, we cannot honor requests for refunds. However, if for some reason you find that the plan you have purchased does not meet your requirements, you may exchange that plan for another plan in our collection within 90 days of purchase. At the time of the exchange, you will be charged a processing fee of 25% of your original plan package price, plus the difference in price between the plan packages (if applicable) and the cost to ship the new plans to you.

Please note: Reproducible drawings can only be exchanged if the package is unopened.

◆ **Building Codes & Requirements** - At the time the construction drawings were prepared, every effort was made to ensure that these plans and specifications meet nationally recognized codes. Our plans conform to most national building codes. Because building codes vary from area to area, some drawing modifications and/or the assistance of a professional designer or architect may be necessary to comply with your local codes or to accommodate specific building site conditions. We advise you to consult with your local building official for information regarding codes governing your area.

Questions? Call Our Customer Service Number
314-770-2228

BLUEPRINT PRICE SCHEDULE — BEST VALUE

Price Code	1-Set	SAVE $110 5-Sets	SAVE $200 8-Sets	Reproducible Masters
AAA	$225	$295	$340	$440
AA	$275	$345	$390	$490
A	$325	$395	$440	$540
B	$375	$445	$490	$590
C	$425	$495	$540	$640
D	$475	$545	$590	$690
E	$525	$595	$640	$740
F	$575	$645	$690	$790
G	$650	$720	$765	$865
H	$755	$825	$870	$970

Plan prices guaranteed through December 31, 2004.
Please note that plans are not refundable.

◆ **Additional Sets*** - Additional sets of the plan ordered are available for $45.00 each. Five-set, eight-set, and reproducible packages offer considerable savings.

◆ **Mirror Reverse Plans*** - Available for an additional $15.00 per set, these plans are simply a mirror image of the original drawings causing the dimensions and lettering to read backwards. Therefore, when ordering mirror reverse plans, you must purchase at least one set of right reading plans.

◆ **One-Set Study Package** - We offer a one-set plan package so you can study your home in detail. This one set is considered a study set and is marked "not for construction." It is a copyright violation to reproduce blueprints.

*Available only within 90 days after purchase of plan package or reproducible masters of same plan.

SHIPPING & HANDLING CHARGES

U.S. SHIPPING	1-4 Sets	5-7 Sets	8 Sets or Reproducibles
Regular *(allow 7-10 business days)*	$15.00	$17.50	$25.00
Priority *(allow 3-5 business days)*	$25.00	$30.00	$35.00
Express* *(allow 1-2 business days)*	$35.00	$40.00	$45.00

CANADA SHIPPING (to/from) - Plans with suffix DR & SH

	1-4 Sets	5-7 Sets	8 Sets or Reproducibles
Standard *(allow 8-12 business days)*	$25.00	$30.00	$35.00
Express* *(allow 3-5 business days)*	$40.00	$40.00	$45.00

Overseas Shipping/International - Call, fax, or e-mail (plans@hdainc.com) for shipping costs.

* For express delivery please call us by 11:00 a.m. Monday-Friday CST